SCOUTING SKETCHES

Scouting Sketches

Lord Hampton, D.S.O.

(*Chief Commissioner, Boy Scouts' Association*)

WITH A FOREWORD BY THE CHIEF SCOUT

The Scout Book Club

The Scout Book Club Edition
Not for sale to the Public

FOREWORD

A MOTOR-CAR is a wonderful contraption of machinery, with its valves, cylinders, electric connections and complicated gears all assembled and neatly fitted to act on each other, but useless as a mobile agent without the addition of the right spirit.

Instruction in the use of these components from an expert is necessary before the would-be motorist can become a driver.

This book, in spite of the gilding—and delightful gilding it is to the reader—is in reality a handbook by an expert, giving the spirit as well as the organisation that makes Scouting to go successfully. It throws a light on the inner feeling as well as the outer form of Scouting. It is full of stories of Scoutcraft founded on fact, and delightfully told, which will not only enlighten parents, teachers, pastors, and public as to the ideals, methods, and possibilities of Scouting, but the sketches are also full of suggestion for Scouters themselves, even those of long experience, as well as for Patrol Leaders and Scouts.

It breathes all through the essential spirit of Scouting—e.g. the Spirit of Service.

Robt Baden-Powell

Scout Book Club Edition . . . . October 1938

CONTENTS

AUTHOR'S FOREWORD

SINCE this book was first published in 1925, I have had a number of kind letters of appreciation from brother Scouts all over the world which encourage me to think that the book has been found not only interesting by them but of value to them in their work.

The Scout Book Club have now done me the honour of suggesting that *Scouting Sketches* should find a place in their growing library. It has not been found possible, however, to issue it in its original form, and a certain amount of cutting has been necessary. As far as possible it has been brought up to date with regard to certain allusions which were applicable when the book was first written but are so no longer.

Slightly differing in its form though it may be, it still carries with it the original dedication: "To my brother Scouts, with best wishes to them in their work for their boys."

HAMPTON.

I.H.Q.
September 14, 1938.

SCOUTING SKETCHES

I

A DREAM—AND AN AWAKENING

IT seemed, as I crouched on the steps of the National Gallery in the bright morning sunshine, that staid old London was full of processions—nothing but processions. They usurped every street leading to the great Square, they obsessed every open space, they crowded unfortunate ordinary mortals like myself between the protecting pillars of friendly doorways or up the wide steps of the larger buildings.

How I ever managed to reach my vantage-point I don't remember—possibly swept along as one of the curious crowd which always hangs upon the flanks of the unusual. All that I *can* recollect is that I found myself perched high above the heads of the surging mass below, my eyes aching with the confusion of marching humanity, my ears numbed by the clashing interests of many bands, and my mind in a complete fog as to the possible meaning of it all.

My first thought of "more unemployed" was strengthened by the banner waving from the plinth of the Nelson Column, which bore the words: "We are unemployed! Give us work for our leisured hours"; and yet a close-up view of a procession even then debouching from Pall Mall only added to my sense of confusion.

For these were no ordinary unemployed, no typical

out-of-works, but young, clean-built, athletic—they looked the pick of our young manhood, of our great schools and universities. And their banner, yellow words on a green ground, was well suited to the spirit of the men who marched beneath it: " Our fathers led in the Great War, let us lead now." Truly a strange wording for an unemployed demonstration, thought I. But even stranger was to follow, for from the direction of the Strand came a second procession, the very opposite of the first. Here were trim, elderly men—retired Generals, Admirals, and Civil Servants at first sight. Above their heads floated the words: " We may be old, but we have grown old in the service of our country. We claim the right to serve and guide the young."

I turned my astonished gaze from them to yet a third procession coming through the Admiralty Arch. Its members wore a variety of costumes and brandished a fine mixture of instruments. Some were in hunting kit, some in the shorts and vests of footballers, others, again, carried bags of golf-clubs, some brandished polo-mallets. There were tennis-rackets, cricket-bats, even skis borne aloft in that motley crowd, representing seemingly the whole world of Sport. Their banner bore the words : " We have learnt to play the game ; we claim the right to teach others." A very noble sentiment, no doubt, but what did it all mean ?

Determined to find out, I descended from my perch and elbowed my way through the crowd in the direction of the dozen or so little platforms from which by now as many orators were holding forth. On my way, with more vigour than tact, I came up against the back of a large but benign constable.

" Steady on, sir," he said ; " you can't hurry here, you know."

" Sorry, constable," I stammered ; " but can you tell me what it's all about ? "

" Well, sir, I don't rightly know that I can, but seemingly they are demanding the right to help in the edication of the youngsters. Everybody's demanding something, and they seem to think that, nowadays, there is more need than ever for training the young idea, so to speak, and that they're the blokes what can do it."

"It's a heavy day for you," I ventured.

"Oh, this is nothing," with an all-embracing wave of the hand. "You go down Victoria way, and you'll see something even stranger."

I accepted this as a hint to move on, and decided to follow out the idea. It was a painful struggle to reach the Admiralty Arch—a struggle enlivened by scraps of rhetoric from many a platform: "The boys who will be the men of to-morrow"; "We can lead, and we will lead"; or again, "War calls for sacrifice of life; peace calls for sacrifice of leisure," and so on in the same lofty strain. But once under the Arch things were easier until I found myself opposite the Palace.

Round the steps of the Queen Victoria Memorial (they had invaded even that) a silent and sympathetic crowd was listening to the impassioned words of yet another orator. I could only get near enough to catch occasional phrases, such as "The greatest Peace Movement of all time"; and, as I turned away, "We have come from the farthest corners of England to help the rising generation of her sons to realise their great heritage."

All very true and fine; but again, what was it all about? I accosted my second constable.

"Why doesn't the Government let them do what they want?" I asked.

Said constable number two: "Well, sir, it ain't exactly a Government matter." He jerked his thumb in the direction of Buckingham Palace Road. "The people at No. 25 down there are the blokes dealing with this little packet. Go and ask them, if you can get in."

It was quite obvious that I couldn't get in, for a queue

four deep stretched from where we stood right down the road in question—a queue admirably marshalled by sundry boys in shorts, shirts, and coloured scarves. I fought my way eventually to No. 25, only to be told that, if I sought entrance thereto, I must wait my turn with the others.

"We are doing what we can," a harassed official replied to my query. "We have had to take over the hotel next door, and still can't deal with all the applicants. What are they applying for? Take one of those special 'buses to Hyde Park, and you'll see."

He indicated a long line of huge vehicles drawn up by the Royal Mews, and constantly moving off as they rapidly filled. I scratched my way to standing space in one of them, and was whisked off to Hyde Park. Arrived there, the most amazing scene of all broke upon my astonished gaze. As far as the eye could see there stretched a medley of camps, each apparently complete in itself.

There were bell-tents, teepees, small squares of canvas, brushwood shelters, log cabins, and many strange woodcraft devices. The nearest one bore the notice, No. 72 Special Training Camp, and contained many men, some young, some old, but all in shirts and shorts, and doing all manner of strange things.

I was about to venture inside to investigate when a young man emerged from a sort of wigwam thing on my right and said: "Show me your warrant, please." . . . And then——

* * * * *

I don't know whether it was the sudden jolt of the slow local, the extreme chilliness of the third-class compartment, or the steady gaze of a pair of grey eyes opposite mine that finally woke me up; but wake I did, to find that the eyes belonged to a poorly-clad boy of fourteen or so. I could see that he wanted to talk, but was too shy to do so without encouragement, so I proceeded to encourage him.

" Cold night," I remarked.

He agreed that it was very cold, and then, pointing to the little badge on my coat lapel asked: " Please, sir, are you a Scoutmaster? "

I admitted the justice of his accusation and returned, " Why, sonny, are you a Scout? " And then the whole story came tumbling out. No, he wasn't a Scout, worse luck, but his brother had been, till he joined the R.A.F., and the Scoutmaster down his way had carried on with great difficulty until ill-health had forced him to give up. There was no Troop now, nor had been for two years, until a few boys got together and tried to carry on by themselves.

" But it wern't no good without a Scoutmaster, sir; and there don't seem to be no one down our way for the job."

I sympathised, and told him all about a Lone Scout I knew away down in a country village. His face brightened.

" Could I be a Lone Scout, too, sir? "

" Why," said I, " do you love the Scouting game as much as all that? "

There was a slight pause, and his face flushed slightly as he murmured, " Not 'arf! "

II

"BUDGE"

(*A story with a moral—mayhap two*)

BUDGE had achieved the age of exactly thirteen years when he joined the village Troop ; and, if I remember rightly, he made his first appearance before his prospective Scoutmaster on the thirteenth day of the month.

Now I am not, I hope, unduly superstitious, but there can be no possible doubt whatever that the history of the two following years proved it to be a most unlucky day in the annals of the 1st Bumblecombe.

Budge came with a bad reputation—in fact, there were those who described him as the wickedest boy in the whole village. What exactly he had done to deserve such a reputation was not vouchsafed by his accusers, but they *did* say that there was nothing in the whole category of juvenile crime which Budge was not capable of committing.

Of course, Budge was not his real name. To be precise, it was James Wilmot, son of old Mrs. Wilmot (Rose Cottage) and James Wilmot, sen., lately deceased.

The boy had had what is called a bad upbringing—an upbringing steeped in the traditions of spirituous liquor. Liquor it was that had driven James, sen., one dark night to a watery grave in the local canal ; and the same agency had deprived old Mrs. Wilmot of much of her former wage-earning capacity.

Budge was the result : a chip off the old block, many said ; a rather ragged chip, too, I fear—such a chip as might be produced by axes—Scout-Woodpecker one, as our wartime Quartermaster would have said. If he had a redeeming quality, it was his grin. I think that he must have been born with that grin on his face. I can almost see him wearing it at his own funeral ; I am quite certain that he would at anyone else's. And it was probably that same grin which finally decided the Scoutmaster to admit him into the Troop, much against the advice, be it said, of the vicar, the schoolmaster, the constable, and many others of the community who represented village opinion.

Nobody quite knows why Budge decided to become a Scout. He was certainly not invited, nor can I believe that he was attracted by the romance and adventure of the great game. It is probable that he scented therein unusual scope for evil-doing and a new field for a perfectly fresh and original series of pranks.

However that may be, the Scoutmaster took upon himself the awful burden of reforming Budge, for he held the opinion that Scouting is not designed only for the boy from a good home ; that the attempt was at least worth the risk it entailed ; and that in the salvation of Budge he might find comforting proof of his own success as a Scoutmaster. Besides which, he liked Budge's grin.

Within a month, however, he began to have grave misgivings as to the wisdom of the step. Scout James Wilmot—he had passed the Tenderfoot Tests with evident boredom but considerable ease—was not shaping well. True, the grin was still there, but a grin alone does not make a Scout, and, taken in conjunction with other things, sometimes becomes a little exasperating.

Budge placed his own original interpretation on the Scout Promise. He seemed, for instance, quite determined to do at least one bad turn every day without receiving any punishment for it. He consistently disobeyed most of the Scout Laws, including, of course, obedience to his Patrol Leader. He got his head smacked for this ; but that made no manner of differcnce, except to broaden the grin.

He made a mock of Troop ceremonies : a live rat at an investiture, a roman-candle in the stove just as the flag was being broken out, the electric light suddenly turned off in the middle of prayers, and many other incidents too numerous to mention.

He got in early one evening and turned all the pictures face to the wall ; he hung the Troop Mascot, a real live black cat, up by her tail to the parallel-bars ; and then, if you please, poured hot sealing-wax down the muzzle of the one and only air-rifle. His language was most unparliamentary, and he frequently formed a separate item on the agenda of the Court-of-Honour.

Often was he sent home half-way through a meeting for some misdemeanour. Once, when this happened—a particularly dark night—Budge retaliated by stretching a cord across the path up to headquarters one foot from the ground, thus causing the undignified collapse of the Assistant Scoutmaster on his face in the mud.

For this crime the Court-of-Honour sentenced him to suspension from the Troop for one calendar month, or eight meetings. During the first two of these work was made difficult by the extraordinary series of noises outside the room, which on investigation came apparently from the chickens in the fowl-run next door or from the twinkling stars above.

The third meeting was marked by a little conspiracy between the Scoutmaster and the constable (also a member of the Troop Committee) whereby Master Budge was captured in *flagrante delicto*, and locked up in the local cell for the night. Thereafter there was peace—such blessed peace that it took our Scoutmaster all his fortitude and singleness of purpose to receive the delinquent back again on the expiration of sentence.

It will occur to many that here, if ever, was an opportunity ready to hand for getting rid of Budge once and for all. Quite apart from his latest effort—that of the stretched cord—there were other reasons which appeared to the Troop Committee to warrant such action. For instance,

Squeak Hobson and Tim Barlow had both been withdrawn by anxious parents from possible contamination, whilst sundry complaints as to poaching threatened a refusal of camping facilities on a site hitherto regarded as Troop property.

But the Scoutmaster was a tenacious man, and held the view that fourteen months of his own influence were insufficient for the purpose of a test case. He argued, moreover, that whereas Squeak and Tim came from good homes and their loss, though deplorable, could be borne, the salvation of Budge (if he could be salved) lay in Scouting for Boys, and in that alone. Besides which, to his keen eyes and alert watchfulness, there were not wanting signs that the boy was yielding ever so slightly to treatment, and that the war between impertinent irresponsibility and firm tact was coming to an end.

Budge, in fact, was finding it increasingly difficult to carry on his share of the struggle against one who met him grin for grin ; who could do everything better than he himself and never swanked about it ; who, however angry he might be, always saw the humour of the situation, and never bore malice ; and who seemed, even to Budge, to be the very embodiment of the Scout Law.

It was obvious that things couldn't go on for ever like this, that one of them would have to give ground. And Budge had a furtive feeling, unexpressed even to himself, that it wouldn't be Scoutmaster.

Nobody knows when the real change began, but I am inclined to think that it dated from a little scene which took place in the Scoutmaster's tent on the first evening of the Whitsun Camp. The *dramatis personæ* were the owner thereof and, of course, Budge, who was metaphorically "on the mat," as usual. The crime, that of stealing money from the Scoutmaster's jacket during bathing. There was no defence. To Budge there could be but one ending. Scoutmaster was speaking quietly, so that only the two most closely concerned could hear.

"Budge, I thought that you and I were friends ; and

yet you could do a thing like that—steal from a friend ! " —Silence.

" Budge, how could you ? "—Still silence, and a hung head for once without a grin.

" Budge, are you sorry ? "—An almost inaudible, " Yes, sir " ; and then, " Am I to go home at once, sir ? "

He ventured to look up, and his gaze was met by a pair of wonderfully kind blue eyes.

" No, Budge ; you are only half a Scout as yet, you know, but I believe that you and I will manage to get there one day. And I believe also, Budge, that you did what you did for your old mother and not for yourself, eh ? "

Budge—the dauntless, irrepressible Budge—was near to tears as he stammered : " Yes, sir. She's been poorly, sir."

" But Budge, lad, why didn't you come to me ? What am I here for if not to help you people ? Anyhow, I don't believe that you will ever do such a thing again. I am ready to risk it at any rate, and I want you to stay in camp and work harder than you have ever worked before. Will you ? "

Came a whisper : " Yes, sir. Scout's Honour, sir." And thus was the armistice signed.

It must not be supposed, however, that Budge became a reformed character from that moment. There was the natural reaction after a long war, and our Scoutmaster was too wise to force matters unduly. It was, indeed, some months later, after many pourparlers, conferences, and minor outbreaks, that peace was finally signed. And it happened in this wise :

Budge had been absent—voluntarily absent—from three consecutive meetings, a most unusual thing for him. So one afternoon the Scoutmaster knocked at the door of Rose Cottage. A querulous " Come in " was the reply, and he entered to find Mrs. Wilmot lying covered with blankets and shawls on a dilapidated sofa.

" Hullo, Mrs. Wilmot ! Are you ill ? " he inquired.

"Well, I 'ave been poorly these last two weeks, sir but I 'ope to be about again soon."

"I'm sorry you've been ill, Mrs. Wilmot. I just called in to ask what has become of Budge these days. He's not been up for a long time."

"He's not had much time, sir, what with looking after me and earning enough to get me medicine. Sir, what's come over Budge? I've never known the boy like it afore. He might be an 'ospital nurse, the way he's looked after me; and him seemin' to know all about it, too. If it's Scoutin' as has done it, all I can say is 'God bless you, sir!' Why, here is the boy. What in 'eaven's name 'ave you been doin' to yourself, son?"

Budge was indeed a pitiable object as he stood grinning in the doorway with water dripping from his clinging garments.

"Gettin' wet, mother, fallin' into the canal," was all his explanation.

"Well, my lad, the best thing you can do now is getting dry falling into fresh clothes," said the Scoutmaster. "And, by the way," he added, "come up if you can next Tuesday—St. George's Day, you know. We want you with us, Budge."

But Tuesday came, and no half-concealed grin broke the solemnity of the proceedings. Rumour was rife in the Troop that night. Hadn't Scoutmaster heard? Budge had gone into the canal and pulled Squeak Hobson out. Squeak had gone down for the third time, when Budge came along and went in with all his clothes on, and had to get Squeak all the way up from the bottom. And now Budge was ill with double pneumonia, and the doctor said he would die—in fact, that he couldn't live through the night. And would he have a Scout's funeral? And would they all have to wear black hat-bands? And was Scoutmaster going to ask for the Silver Cross for him?

Most of these questions were pressed upon an anxious-eyed man hastily getting into his coat, and all were left unanswered as he started at a run for Rose Cottage.

The first person he met was the doctor, just leaving. His remarks were brief and reassuring. "Lord bless you, no! he's not going to die. One lung a bit touched up, that's all. He's going on well. And, Jack," he added, "that's a gallant lad you've got. We shouldn't have known anything about it if it hadn't been for young Hobson talking. Gave him artificial respiration, too, Budge did; and then carried him home, and told him he'd throw him back again if he said anything about it. Gallant lad! Good-night."

"So that was your getting wet, Budge, was it?" said the Scoutmaster a few minutes later, in a voice just a little bit husky, as he contemplated a much-subdued and feverish Budge in bed.

He was greeted with a ghost of a grin, and had to bend his head over the boy to catch his reply: "Sir, do you remember that time in camp when you said I was only 'alf a Scout?"

"Yes, Budge, I remember."

"Am I a whole Scout yet, sir?"

The Scoutmaster smiled as he replied gently: "Yes, Budge, I think we may safely say that you've arrived at last; and you're a bit of a hero, too, you know. But the doctor said I mustn't let you talk, and here we are chattering like a pair of magpies. Buck up and get fit again, and I'll look in to-morrow. Good-night!"

"Good-night, sir, and thank you."

The Scoutmaster turned at the door. "Thank me! What for, you young rascal?"

Budge flushed a deeper red as he replied: "For all you've rubbed into me in the Scouts, sir."

"Well, there we are quits, Budge, for you've rubbed into *me* a fact worth all of that."

The boy looked puzzled, as well he might.

"That God is very good, Budge." With this cryptic remark the Scoutmaster closed the door softly behind him and passed out into the night. And, as he went, his face wore a happy smile, and his soul was filled with a great content.

III

THE EARLY DAYS

I

I HAVE just related to you the moving story of Budge. If you have honoured me by reading it through, it is possible that you will agree with a certain Scoutmaster friend of mine, who has confided to me that, on the whole, he considers the last state of that youth to be worse than the first, and that he can see James Wilmot, jun., turning into a prig of the first water. I see his point, but I don't agree with his reasoning.

No doubt if I were to continue the history of that young gentleman in the same vein as that which obtained at the close of its first chapter, I should relate to you how, having risen from his bed of sickness, he donned once more his Scout uniform and, in the presence of the whole village—including, of course, his comrades of the 1st Bumblecombe—had a small Silver Cross attached to his breast by the local District Commissioner.

This ceremony would be followed by his promotion first to Patrol Leader (with heads of his own to smack), and finally to the honoured position of Troop Leader and pride of the village.

As a matter of fact, only the first of these desirable happenings actually took place. The Silver Cross was duly attached to a very torn shirt, and the whole village could testify to the immensity of the grin which suffused the face of Budge during the proceedings.

As for the rest, he left the Troop within the following

six months, and is now, I am told, one of His Majesty's able-bodied seamen. I cannot imagine a prig thriving 'tween-decks of a battle-cruiser.

However that may be, I have an uneasy feeling that I have been harping on the wrong string; or, to express myself more clearly, have acted like a novelist who begins writing his novel at Chapter XXII, with a view to working outwards from that point.

My original intention had been to lift for a moment before your eyes the veil of mystery which enshrouds the earliest days of the 1st Bumblecombe Troop of B-P. Scouts, and to display to your sympathetic understanding all those little struggles, disappointments, and occasional triumphs which are part and parcel of the early history of most similar ventures.

For I take it that we learn as much from failures (whether on the part of others or of ourselves) as we do from successes; and at any rate it is comforting to read of another happy band of brothers who started out under difficulties similar perhaps to our own, and who in common with so many did that which they ought not to have done, and equally left undone those things which they most certainly should have performed.

Therefore, with your kind permission, I will try to start this time in the right place, at the beginning of things.

The 1st Bumblecombe (pronounced Bunkum, in no sense of disparagement, but merely as a local abbreviation) was always an obscure Troop. It had its being in an obscure village of small pretensions and population. In fact, I have never been able to discover why its members should have adopted the prefix "First," because under no stretch of the imagination could there ever have been a second; there were not enough boys to go round.

What boys there were, however, appear to have had the right spirit, for history relates that the first handful started blithely out on to the great ocean of Scouting without any thought of the possible convenience of a Scoutmaster.

In the beginning there were ten of them—not little nigger boys, although very grimy in patches. And it all came about because one of their number, who rejoiced in the alarming name of Squid, won a prize given for the best essay on the adventures of the annual Choir Outing, this same prize being a copy of *Scouting for Boys*.

That sealed the fate of the village as far as Scouts were concerned, in spite of the fact that the Rector, in his abysmal ignorance, didn't hold with Scouts—" organised mischief " is what he called it—and I am bound to say, for the first few months of the great adventure, he was not far off the mark.

There is no doubt that *Scouting for Boys* was absorbed by the gang with a zest which might well be copied by many a Scoutmaster. Its torn and dog-eared pages became indescribably filthy, its nice red cover disappeared for good within a week, and I firmly believe that every member, from the great Squid himself down to Tubby James, could have passed with honours an examination, written and *viva voce*, upon its contents.

The question of a leader resolved itself naturally. There could be no disputing Squid's authority, quite apart from his ownership of the book. He was a big, strong boy, and had been accustomed to lead by virtue both of physical and moral ascendancy. He was a likeable boy too, and had what is called " a way with him." Besides all of which, he could kick a football farther and with greater accuracy than any of his contemporaries.

But I must admit that, though his superficial knowledge of the wonderful book was hard to fault, his interpretation thereof left something to be desired. After all, he was only fourteen, and at fourteen we suck the sugar and throw away the pill. It is only natural, therefore, that their early efforts were chiefly concerned with the acquiring of headquarters and a very strange assortment of what they were pleased to style uniform. Most of them wore shorts and all of them shirts, of a kind, in everyday life, so these presented no difficulty. Poles they cut from a convenient coppice without permission; old red bandana handkerchiefs were knotted round their throats, and their haversacks ranged from school satchels to bits of sacking. Knives were of all sorts and sizes, and they possessed but three whistles; but that didn't matter in the least. What did matter was the question of head-gear.

In the beginning only one of them possessed a Scout hat, to wit, Sam Jones, whose father sold picture postcards, bootlaces and tobacco for his own benefit in the intervals of dispensing stamps and telegraph forms for the benefit of His Majesty's Government. Sam's hat was for long the envy of all beholders, and, needless to say, he wore it with a self-conscious pride which goaded the rest of the gang to most un-Scoutlike resentment.

Hats they must have; but the question was how? Ways and means were anxiously debated at headquarters. By the way, I quite forgot to describe that edifice or the method of its acquisition. You should know that Buster's grandfather's estate consisted of a small orchard, with a still smaller meadow attached thereto. At one end of the meadow Providence had deposited a lean-to—only Providence could tell you why. Let us assume that the inevitability of the Scout Movement was the reason.

The method of its acquisition was simple in the extreme. Buster was deputed to negotiate, with the result that the shed was "let" to the 1st Bumblecombe in return for an undertaking on the part of Squid and Co. to supply free labour on the estate whenever and wherever required. It says something for the boys that they faithfully carried out their share of the bargain, and even continued it long after the shed had been given up on removal to larger premises. Perhaps free access to the apples in the orchard had something to do with this; but that is another story altogether.

The fitting up of headquarters was the next difficulty. There was in the first place the problem of closing up the front, and, although it only measured sixteen feet by eight, it was some time before sufficient brushwood, unconsidered trifles of planking, a rusty galvanised-iron sheet, and sundry old sacks could be scrounged for the purpose.

Of interior decoration there was none. The walls were entirely innocent of charts, Carlos pictures, Patrol insignia, or Scout Law poster. Not even a document to say that the 1st Bumblecombe was registered at Imperial Headquarters; and I regret to say that up to date that august body had been vouchsafed no opportunity of becoming aware of their existence. The only adornment was a Union Jack, one of those cheap affairs which schoolchildren love to flaunt on patriotic occasions, and which are, I imagine, printed off at the rate of so many thousand per minute with no one by to see that they are even printed straight. The furniture consisted of two packing-cases and three old fruit-baskets, and a table made out of an ancient wooden door. Such was the home of the 1st Bumblecombe. We can now return to the hats.

Miss Simpkins solved this question. Miss Simpkins was one of those people who make a habit of solving pressing questions of finance in small village communities. She taught in Sunday-school, she ran a Mother's Union, she was Hon. Secretary of the Nursing Fund and goodness knows how many other funds besides, and she annually made herself responsible for the organisation of the village concert and such whist drives as the needs of the moment might require.

The village could not possibly have existed without her—in fact, I must confess that many regarded her as far more necessary than the Rector. It was natural, therefore, that at a specially convened meeting of the Troop it should have been decided to apply to this good lady for assistance.

The trouble was that Miss Simpkins did not number *Scouting for Boys* amongst the classics in her small but select library, and could not, therefore, be expected to understand the pressing need for a certain type of hat. But she was a woman of sympathetic and very human understanding and with an abiding love for children, and she looked at life through rosy spectacles out of a pair of eyes which were seldom without a sparkle of humour.

Thus it was that, when a deputation consisting of Squid, Buster, and Sam called upon her armed with the great book, she listened to their confused exposition with becoming gravity, and thereafter regaled them with tea, buns, and chocolate cake. The net result of the interview was as satisfactory as the manner of it ; for it transpired that the choir were in urgent need of new surplices, and that Miss Simpkins had already decided to organise a whist drive with a view to putting the matter right. What, therefore, could be more natural than that Scout hats and surplices should join forces as an excuse for a pleasant evening.

When the deputation was finally ushered forth into the dusk, the dingy volume which had been the cause of all the trouble was left behind at Miss Simpkins's request. She was a keen student of human nature, and she was determined to find out, now that the opportunity was to hand, wherein lay the charm of this Scouting, of which she had heard much but seen nothing—a charm which could seize the imagination of a few thoughtless village boys, and cause Master Squid to say (rather self-consciously perhaps, but with evident purpose) as he saluted on leaving : " You can count on the Troop, miss, if there's ever a job you want seen to."

So observe Miss Simpkins, her horn-rimmed spectacles carefully adjusted, her little feet out-thrust to a cheerful blaze, and her agile mind immersed in *Scouting for Boys*.

She laid it down some two hours later. It had not, of course, been possible to do more than skim its pages in that time, but an observer would have noticed that she turned back more than once to Camp-Fire Yarn

No. 4, and that it was this same three pages which she re-read before the book was finally laid aside.

"I think I understand," she murmured to herself. "Anyhow, bless the boys! I'll see this thing through."

2

I have already persuaded you, I hope, that Miss Simpkins was a woman of sympathy and understanding. I ought now to add that she was also a person of determination and method.

She never did anything unless she had previously determined in her own mind that it was well worth the doing. When, and if, she so determined, she set about the doing of it with commendable thoroughness and ability.

It was quite obvious that the book *Scouting for Boys* had gripped her imagination. It is a remarkable thing, if you come to think of it, that the same volume can appeal in equal measure to an elderly lady (who would never see another sixty-second birthday) and to a handful of youngsters, whose united years barely totalled double that figure. Personally I can think of few books which have accomplished such a phenomenon as this; but it is perhaps equally true to add that the reasons for its attraction are not identical.

I can understand what Squid and Co. thought about it; to them it was a novel exposition of life such as they had never received before. It satisfied their boyhood imagination in a way hitherto unheard of. It is all very well to read books such as *Sherlock Holmes*, *Treasure Island*, *Robinson Crusoe*, and *The Last of the Mohicans*, and to have nice little talks in Sunday-school about King Arthur and his Knights of the Round Table, but it is quite a different thing to have all these exciting and wondrous adventures put up in tabloid form like a lot of enchanted pills in a box, so that by the simple process of sucking one you can turn yourself into a delightful combination of all those old heroes of adventure and chivalry.

There was naturally much written down in those well-thumbed pages which as yet they had been unable to grasp. The sections dealing with Organisation and Troop Management left them singularly cold, and I regret to have to record that even those which explained to them the Scout Law were amongst the cleanest in the book. The fact remains, however, that their young enthusiasm had been fired, and that it takes something rather exceptional to do that with even the youthful dwellers in the village of Bumblecombe.

Miss Simpkins accepted the book with equal enthusiasm, but in a somewhat different spirit. She, too, in spite of her advancing years, loved tales of adventure; she was wont to declare that they kept her young. But to her ripe intelligence was given the power to delve below the written word, to search out motives, and to visualise possibilities. She had an unshaken belief in and love for her countrymen; she was also a keen student of the problems of Empire; and so it was that, even in those early half-fledged days, she could gather the skeins together and weave a wonderful future for this Brotherhood of Youth.

But she did not stop there—at mere dreams. She was a modest little woman it is true; but, even so, loved to think of herself as in some part responsible for the life and thought of her little community. Everything that was good for it was her personal care, and she made up her mind, after due deliberation and further perusal of Squid's grimy volume, that Scouting was good for Bumblecombe. That being so, Bumblecombe had to have Scouting. There was absolutely no way out of it.

It is significant to note that Miss Simpkins did not consult the Rector. Not that she failed to acknowledge the authority of Rectors generally, in their own sphere; but she had already acted as churchwarden to his two predecessors, and thought of incumbents rather as

Secretaries of State, nominally responsible perhaps, but with herself as permanent Under-Secretary, the one who possessed the real knowledge and possibly the greater ability to make use of it. Besides which, she did not find herself invariably in agreement with his point of view. He was narrow, she considered, and far too prone to vent his pompous indignation or cynical wit on many subjects which he had never even taken the trouble to study or to understand. He had, for instance, called this Scouting game "organised mischief," but had never read the book which gave it life. He was fond of referring to his village boys as "some of life's little trials," but was apparently incapable of seeing that the guiding of those same little trials was at least one of his first duties as pastor.

It was fortunate, indeed, for the boys of Bumblecombe that there was a Miss Simpkins in the offing, a real Fairy Godmother of rare understanding and active imagination—one, moreover, who loved them for their youth and for all the promise of the years to come.

Without a Miss Simpkins it is very certain, for instance, that those hats could not have been produced with such miraculous ease.

There were other things, too, besides hats—a serviceable candle-lamp and two pictures, a chart of the Scout Law and a small bookshelf, all very necessary and useful when you come to think of it.

Needless to say, they were not all of them the result of the whist drive. Such functions, even when organised by a Miss Simpkins, are strictly limited as regards their financial possibilities. This one sufficed for the hats and the chart (with something over for the surplices), but as for the rest, they were the result of Squid and Sam being turned into the Simpkins lumber-room with leave to rummage for anything which might be useful.

There was a wealth of treasure of surpassing value in that lumber-room; but, stricken with a quite unusual shyness, the two decided that it would not be playing the game to take too much ; and that the pictures, the lamp and bookshelf would in themselves be great additions to the somewhat spare furnishing of headquarters.

I agree about the last two, but I am not so sure about the pictures. The first was that well-known but somewhat melancholy representation of the defeated Napoleon on the deck of the *Bellerophon*, and the second an ancient engraving of " Souls in Torment " from Dante's *Inferno*. But they were pictures, which was the main thing ; and, as Sam remarked, if they hung the " Souls in Torment " over that hole in the end wall it would lessen the draught. If he had understood the full significance of the picture, he might have added that such a position would also conduce to the cooling of the poor souls.

They showed their treasures to Miss Simpkins before leaving, who agreed that, if their taste in art was at present somewhat undeveloped, the pictures were at least better than bare walls, and would do until others more appropriate could be found. And so the incident closed. But there was a sequel.

Miss Simpkins was an early riser, being in the habit of pottering round her small garden before breakfast in order, so she said, to make good the horticultural deficiencies of her two-days-a-week gardener. But it happened that on a certain morning about a fortnight after the delivery of the hats she rose from her bed at the late hour of 8.30 ; and she would have been inclined to blame herself greatly for such laziness if it had not been for a truly astonishing sight which met her eyes while in the act of gauging the weather from the window.

Down below was her small square of lawn being sedulously rolled by Master Squid, while beyond was Jimmy (the porter's boy) intent on the task of weeding the kitchen garden. Both were too deeply engaged to take note of the little lady at the window ; and, like a wise person, she decided not to spoil the idyll by making her presence known.

With a little glow of excitement, therefore, she ensconced herself behind one of the lace curtains in a position which admitted of an uninterrupted view of the proceedings. These, however, soon terminated. The roller was carefully returned to its accustomed place behind the potting-shed, Squid put on his coat, and summoned his companion in labour in a voice carefully toned to the occasion, "School bell! Come on"; and as the two passed immediately below the window, he remarked: "That's done the pictures; we'll do the shelf and lamp to-morrow."

While the sole witness of this moving episode hurriedly dressed herself, two thoughts were uppermost in her mind: the one of thankfulness for having overslept, and the other a strong desire that the conventions could be overcome sufficiently to allow of the Rector sharing her private view on the morrow.

3

Our little lady was in the habit of paying fortnightly visits to the local market town, situate some six and a half miles from the village of Bumblecombe. She invariably made a day of it, combining the business (and pleasure) of shopping with the pleasure (and business) of a round of visits to personal cronies.

When fine and dry, Miss Simpkins rode her tricycle; if wet or threatening, the services of the father of all Fords were commandeered from the local garage.

On the present occasion there was a south-west wind combined with a falling glass—undoubtedly a Ford day.

Her first call was at the shop of W. Brown and Sons, booksellers and stationers, and the proprietors of the only circulating library in the district. Mr. Brown was one of the pillars of society, a personal friend of half the town, and a safe authority on the latest novels. He hastened forward at once, and, after the usual and necessary preliminaries about the weather, remarked that he had especially kept back a copy of *When Autumn Goes*—quite the rage just now, and a book which he could personally recommend.

"Thanks, I'll take it," replied Miss Simpkins ; "and, by the way," she added, "a new and little-known disease has broken out amongst the village children, and I want a copy of any work you may have dealing with it."

Mr. Brown looked deferentially grave.

"I'm sure I'm sorry to hear that," he said, "but perhaps it will only turn out to be measles, after all—at least, let us hope so."

He led the way to where a set of steps gave access to the higher shelves, and mounted until his hand could reach the row marked "Medical Works."

"We do not carry a large stock of these," he said, as he ran his hand along the row of backs, "but I can confidently rccommend *Child Ailments and How to Cure Them.*" He withdrew the volume in question and handed it down. Miss Simpkins was quite enjoying her little joke, and her eyes danced as she replied: "But the trouble is, Mr. Brown, that I want to spread this disease, not cure it."

The little man looked puzzled, as well he might, but he was enlightened by the lady's next remark and by the unmistakable twinkle in the eyes which looked up into his own. "The malady goes by the name of 'Scouting,'" she explained, "and the book I want is *Scouting for Boys*, by Sir Robert Baden-Powell."

Mr. Brown beamed. "Well now, just fancy you mentioning that. My boy, Bill, he's gone for a Scout. They had a meeting in the Parish Room a week ago and have started a Troop, or whatever they call it. Young Grainger's Scoutmaster, so I've heard; though what good he'll do, him with no army training, I don't see. But Bill's keen, and nothing would do for him but to join up. Not that I hold with this soldiering, but Mrs. Brown thinks that it won't do him any real harm, and Bill is one as is hard to turn once his mind's made up. Got me to order half a dozen copies of your book ; said as they'd go like wildfire, but your's is the first inquiry as I've had yet."

"Never mind, Mr. Brown," was the reply; "I'll help by taking two copies. I've got to find a Scoutmaster for Bumblecombe somehow, and he'll want to know what to do when I've found him. Oh, and just a piece of advice: Keep one of the remaining copies and read it yourself. I'm sure you'll like it better than *When Autumn Goes*. Good morning."

Little Miss Simpkins tripped away up the street with her parcel, conscious of having had the last word, and leaving the surprised bookseller to rearrange his medical shelf.

I need not dwell in detail upon the rest of her day. Like most of its predecessors, it consisted in a few more shops, a committee meeting, lunch with Miss Adams at the fine old Queen Anne house next the church, another committee meeting, and finally tea at the Hall with Mrs. Jamieson.

This last episode calls, perhaps, for a passing mention. It transpired that Colonel Jamieson had taken the chair, somewhat unwillingly, at the afore-mentioned Scout meeting, but had returned home mollified in the belief that he had made a considerable impression with his chairman's remarks. During tea, as was to be expected, he regaled the visitor with extracts from the more telling of these.

"Quite a good meeting, considering the night," he said. "Fine thing, this Scout Movement—just what the boys need, drill and discipline with capital D's, and plenty of it. Why, when I was a youngster——" And so on.

Miss Simpkins knew from her past experience of the old gentleman that it was quite useless to attempt to speak until he had finished. She had tried once, and had simply been whisked away like a straw in Niagara. The present occasion was no exception, for steam was up, and the Colonel was running quite smoothly and non-stop. It must have been nearly ten minutes before the flow was rudely interrupted by his cigar-ash falling inside his bulging waistcoat, and he subsided with a naughty word into the nearest arm-chair.

"By the way," ventured the lady, "have you ever read the book?"

The Colonel, having finally hunted the ash to safety, made reply: "Book! What book? Never knew there was a book. Oh, that!" he went on, as he adjusted his pince-nez and took the volume from Miss Simpkins's hands. "No, can't say I have."

"I thought you probably hadn't," she said sweetly. "Funny thing, but I've read it through twice, and there's hardly anything about drill in it. And if I were you, Colonel, I should look at Yarn No. 4; that seems to be the crux of the whole thing. I'll lend you that copy if you like. Read it right through, and don't send it back until you've finished with it."

Having thus sown her second lot of seed, Miss Simpkins departed in the direction of the garage, where her ancient vehicle was wont to rest its aching frame.

As it came to a standstill before her own door half an hour later, she espied Master Squid in his Scout uniform, with the new hat set jauntily on the back of his head, wheeling a broken-down perambulator in her direction.

"Doing your good turn to the baby?" she suggested.

Squid saluted and grinned. "No, miss, this ain't a perambulator," he replied; "it's our trek-cart, and I'm taking some spuds into camp."

Miss Simpkins was deeply interested. "Oh, you're in camp, are you? That's splendid. And where are you camping?"

The boy looked rather shame-faced. "Well, it ain't exactly camping, miss, because we haven't got a tent; but some of us is sleeping in the hut, and we do our own cooking, and go scouting, and——"

Here the lady interrupted. "How jolly that must be,

Squid! I'm coming to tea with you next Saturday afternoon."

Squid's face fell quite two degrees. "Oh, it's all right; I'll bring my own mug, and perhaps something else; and you shall give me my tea like Australian bushmen, and show me the hut."

The boy's face cleared again. "It was the mug I was thinkin' about, miss. But we should be glad if you'd come, and not mind a bit of dirt," he added, and, saluting, turned away and trundled on down the street.

Miss Simpkins's eyes followed his retreating form into the dusk, and the fact was borne in upon her mind that the handle of the stick was in the hands of Squid and Co., while Mr. Brown and the Colonel were for the moment dangling hopelessly at the wrong end.

4

I once heard the view expressed that no boy under the age of sixteen years is capable of connected thought for more than one minute at a time. I rather think that the author of this severe dictum can have had little experience of the young animals. He was probably relieving his surcharged feelings on the subject of boys generally.

Personally, I have known quite small specimens of their kind who, at any rate, gave the appearance of connected thought for much longer periods than one minute. Of course, the question as to whether it was all one long thought or an unbroken series of short ones would be difficult to decide unless one had the opportunity of observing the after-result.

Whatever may be the expert psychological answer to this difficult question, it is quite certain that the great Squid was capable of considerable concentration; and I think that in this Miss Simpkins would have agreed with me if she could have seen him at about 3 p.m. on the Saturday following their meeting. But, according to arrangements, the lady was not due at the hut until

4.30, and it happened to be the imminence of her arrival which accounted for the concentration of Squid.

It was a perfect day for this type of exercise. The sky above was a dome of azure, the meadow a carpet of flowers. The little brook which bordered it burbled lazily over its bed of potted-meat tins to the dragon-flies flirting overhead. Larks sang, bees hummed, and innumerable flies buzzed cheerily as they scavenged the pile of unwashed plates by the camp-fire. In short, a typical English day in early summer.

But Squid had no eyes for Nature's beauty all around him. He was seated in company with Sam and Buster on the floor of the hut. They found the floor was convenient, and also safer, than either the fruit-baskets or the packing-cases, one of which latter, by the way, had been fed to the fire ten minutes ago owing to a lack of coarser fuel.

There was, indeed, much to trouble their minds, for it seemed that one problem safely overcome led but to another yet more intricate, as if, indeed, a sombre fate was intervening to ensure that the course of true Scouting should not run too smooth. They were beginning to learn in a practical manner that few things in life really worth having can be obtained without a struggle, and that success comes only to those who, failing the gift of genius, are content to woo it with the sweat of their brow.

Quite early in the life of the 1st Bumblecombe—in fact, within a week of its formation—dire dissensions had arisen. Even the authority of the chosen leader had been challenged, heads had been smacked, posteriors kicked, and anon, I regret to say, sundry tears shed. These early troubles had led to a reduction in strength, but it is probable that the six who now remained were the survival of the fittest, and, for that reason, the more likely to throw the shoots of a successful Troop.

Another problem had been the roof of headquarters. As originally taken over, it leaked in sixteen places—

Buster had carefully counted them—but, on the other hand, Sam, the arch-scrounger, had annexed an old tarpaulin, destined for service as a tent. This useful article had given rise to one of the bitterest problems of all. Sam opined that, as it had been given for a tent, for a tent it should be used. Squid affirmed that one good roof was better than two bad ones; while Buster—always a bright boy—suggested that they could use it as a tent when fine and as an extra roof when wet. This seemed a brilliant solution until it was discovered to contain flaws in practice, because they found that the process of dragging the tarpaulin from off the roof and replacing it thereon disintegrated the thatch to such a degree that confusion became worse confounded. Thereupon Squid had asserted himself. "We'll get a tent somehow," he said, and proceeded to nail the tarpaulin securely to the outside roof-beams. And that was that.

The present difficulty was perhaps more subtle, if less complicated, than either of those recorded above—nothing more, in fact, than the question of a seat for their guest of the afternoon, but they hadn't thought of it until almost too late. There were, of course, the remaining packing-cases; but, as Sam remarked, they could hardly ask a lady to risk a seat which had already been proved and found wanting. One fruit-basket was in a like state of dilapidation, and the other had been used recently for the solemn rite of skinning a rabbit. There remained the grass; but that, again, was slightly damp from a night of rain, and they had no ground-sheets. Of course, the obvious solution would appear to be an appeal to Buster's grandfather; but unfortunately the boys were under a cloud in that quarter, owing to the fact that the very early morning of the last week-end had been made hideous for all who wooed slumber within half a mile of the hut. Only Buster's superior agility had saved him from the grandpaternal stick when he next called for the milk, and he had been warned at the same time that the contract between the two parties might be considered terminable without notice if such a thing occurred again.

Sam's suggestion that he (Buster) should go over and ask for the loan of a chair had been received with the disdain it deserved. It really was a most tactless suggestion, and fully earned Buster's derision. "You can go yourself, Sammy boy; grand-dad said he'd wallop me if I got within range of that stick, and I aren't goin'. Guess I'll let him cool a bit longer." Eminently sound, no doubt, but unproductive.

However, Miss Simpkins as a solver of problems did not belie her reputation; nor, as a good fairy, did she fail to appear in the nick of time. She was almost too soon—at least for Jimmy, Alf, and Tubby (*alias* James Mings), who were lying prostrate by the brook-side clothed in nothing but shorts. It was Buster's bright eye which spied the top of her hat coming down the lane from the village, and it was also Buster's raucous young voice which was raised in timely admonition to the three. Then ensued a period of frantic diving into shirts, stockings and hats, for it would never do to receive their guest in anything less than full uniform.

Even Squid, the imperturable Chief, might have been observed passing a surreptitious comb through overlong hair, while Sam, always careful of a very prepossessing appearance, pulled his belt straight and readjusted the bandana about his neck. Buster confined himself to shouting directions and upsetting the kettle.

However, all was in order, and the boys standing at the salute, when the lady reached camp; and furthermore, it was noticed with considerable relief and some curiosity that she carried in one hand a camp-stool and in the other a basket covered by a neat white cloth.

From the first Miss Simpkins dominated the situation. She had a habit of dominating situations, and it is doubtful whether there had ever been one more suited to her taste than the present.

" Good-afternoon, everyone," she began. " I haven't learnt the proper Scout salute yet, but I'm going to shake you all by the left hand."

This was done. " Now, while you boil the kettle, Squid shall show me round, and then we'll have tea. There's a great big cake and other things in that basket. And after tea I think we'll just sit round the fire and talk about the Troop. Shall we ? "

Chorus : " Yes, miss ; *rather*, miss ! " The ice was broken and formality banished.

Squid and Miss Simpkins entered the hut ; Tubby explored the basket and set out the cake and other things ; Buster refilled the kettle and set it on the fire, while the rest undertook a belated and perfunctory washing of the plates and mugs in the brook.

There is no doubt about the success of that meal. The cake was very popular, and if the tea was not quite up to bush standard, at least Miss Simpkins expressed complete approval, and actually asked for a second mugful. As Buster said afterwards, " It can't have been all that bad."

When they had finished, plates and mugs were thrown aside on the grass and expectant looks directed towards their guest. Possibly they felt that the next hour was likely to be an important one in the history of the 1st Bumblecombe. But Miss Simpkins had been round the camp with Squid, and her quick eyes had noticed several things of which she was sure the Chief Scout would not approve.

Like a wise person, she had no intention of usurping Squid's authority ; and so it was Squid, well primed beforehand, who divided his forces and issued orders.

" Sam, take your bike and ride back to ' The Shrubbery ' for a spade. Buster, you and Jim will wash the plates and things ; the rest, under me, will take off stockings and get all them tins out of the brook—then we'll bury 'em."

" That's better," said Miss Simpkins, when all was

done to her satisfaction. " I hate untidiness. Now we can talk about the Troop. Perhaps I had better do most of the talking. Shall I ? "

General assent.

" Well, in the first place, you are all keen on this Scouting, aren't you ? "

General assent.

" But there are not quite enough of you for a Troop, so you had better be one Patrol to start with. What name shall we choose ? "

All sorts of suggestions, some practical, some not.

" Don't you think that you ought to choose an animal which makes an easy noise ? "

Up spake Buster. " Yes, miss ; an owl, miss. I can do an owl."

" That's a good idea, Buster ; but can you all do an owl ? "

Chorus of owls—quite good owls, too.

" That's first-rate. What about it, Squid—will you be the Owl Patrol ? Right ! That's one thing fixed, at any rate. Now, I have been reading the book, and I've found out a lot of interesting things about Scouts. One is that you are not real Scouts at all until you've passed the Tenderfoot Tests and taken the Scout Promise. Have they been learning any of the Tests, Squid ? "

" They've done a bit, miss," said the boy. " We can most of us do the Signs and Salute, and I know the Union Jack and the Law. But they don't work at it as they should. They're always playing about."

" I rather expect they are," said Miss Simpkins, " so I have got a suggestion to make. I am going to try and find a Scoutmaster for you, but until I do, you can all come up to me twice a week, and we will work at the Tests together. What do you say ? "

Needless to relate, the resolution was passed unanimously, and when the lady left a few minutes later it was generally agreed that the future of the Troop was assured.

5

When I was a boy at school—more years ago now than I care to remember—the authorities had a habit of issuing once a term a compilation of amateur effort called the School Magazine (*alias* " The Magger ").

I was not a contributor, seldom even a steady reader, of this publication, and as far as I can recollect "The Magger" did not often contain anything worth reading. But there was one exception, and that was a list of the names of the cricket eleven and the football fifteen, together with a criticism of their talents, which appeared at the close of the cricket and football terms respectively. This list, even if one did not happen to be a member of one of those august bodies, was always eagerly read and commented upon; and, looking back over the lapse of years, I can understand how very good it must have been for those concerned to have their virtues or faults held up in this way to the admiration or derision (as the case might be) of their world.

I can even conceive that the anonymous critic at times administered a rude shock to their pride.

For instance, young "A," who was used to being told by many admirers that he was one of the fastest wing three-quarters that the school had ever seen, and had come in consequence to believe it, might see written down in cold print the statement that "'A,' when he acquires pace and can use his head, may make a useful wing three-quarter"; while "B," who fancied himself as a fast bowler, would be quietly but firmly put in his place by such words as, "'B,' in spite of having shown himself fairly consistent in the field, will have to work hard to retain his place in the side." Sometimes very cruel, but always salutary.

You may ask what all this has to do with the 1st Bumblecombe, or, indeed, with Scouts at all. The connection lies in the fact that one of the first things Miss Simpkins did after that memorable picnic was to compile a list of the boys, together with brief notes on their home upbringing, and the result thereof. To these she gradually added various characteristics as they were made apparent on closer acquaintance. This document was not intended for publication, but was merely anticipating the day when she could turn the Troop over as a going concern to the Scoutmaster of her choice.

Quite rightly she determined that the first thing he would want to know was something about the material upon which his experiments in character training were to be made.

I was interested when I heard of this effort, because such a thing had never occurred to me before, and I have occasionally wondered since whether any Scoutmaster keeps a similar book.

In Miss Simpkins's case the idea was probably due to her passion for method in all she undertook. For many years she had kept a detailed personal diary, and her minutes of meetings were models of what such things should be. So I suppose it was but natural that the respective characters of the 1st Bumblecombe should be as carefully studied and committed to writing.

I don't know what the boys themselves would have thought about it; and it might be interesting to try the effect of the regular publication of a document of this sort upon the members of a Troop. No doubt it would cause more merriment than anything else, and I hardly think that the posting of the fact that "Scout 'A,' height four foot nothing, makes more noise than his size warrants," would have the effect of quietening Scout "A"; or that an improvement in the appearance of Scout "B" could be brought about by his public description as "consistently the dirtiest boy in the Troop."

But it is quite certain that if a full record were to be kept of the upbringing, character, Scout history, and final result of every boy in the Troop much food for thought would be forthcoming.

Thus a Scoutmaster might find that Scout "C,"

quick and intelligent above the ordinary, had amassed Proficiency Badges as Engineer, Electrician and Airman, with a final note to the effect that he had left the Troop for the purpose of looking after Farmer Jones's pigs; or that Scout "D," who had spent a considerable time in decorating himself as a Beekeeper, Gardener and Cyclist, but had omitted to learn how to swim, had, like Budge, ended up in the Royal Navy.

But, like Miss Simpkins, we realise that badges are but one of the many means to be utilised in the self-education of the boy; and, as far as the Owl Patrol was concerned, we can be content to gain some impression of its material from a précis of her crisp and businesslike notes.

Thus we learn that Squid, whose father had died when he was three, had determination and initiative, and, while perhaps of a slow intellect, was exceeding sure and very straight. Miss Simpkins conceived him to be a natural leader and a sound influence on the other boys.

Sam Jones, now a corporal (as it was called in those days), had been a spoilt darling until he went to the local grammar school. There he had developed into a fine young athlete, and had shed most of his nonsense in the process. He was invariably clean and knew how to put on his uniform to the best effect; but a note informs us that he was inclined to be lazy at anything unconnected with running, swimming and games generally.

Buster, on the other hand, was irrepressible and facetious. He shouted for preference when a whisper would have sufficed. He gambolled through life like a kitten, and was with difficulty persuaded to wash his knees. He was full of unsound advice upon every conceivable subject, but was an attractive little fellow for all that, bubbling over to help (whether or no help was required), and as keen as mustard. His real name was John Butcher, but his father had for long called him Buster after a favourite dog (now deceased), and the name suited him to perfection.

Then we come to Tubby, or properly James Mings. There was not much in the book about Tubby. He was lethargic and apparently guileless, and his figure seemed to cry out for an intensive course of P.T.

The next entry belongs to Alfred Evers, whom Miss Simpkins found quite different to the others. His people had only recently come to the neighbourhood from Manchester, and he was physically weaker but mentally more alert than the Bumblecombe boys. Clever and inclined to precocity, but well mannered.

Very different to him was the last on the list, Jimmy Cape (son of old Cape, the porter). Jimmy for his size was the strongest boy in the Patrol. He had run wild from a babe, and was the leading spirit of a close combination consisting of himself and Buster. Like the latter, he seldom washed his knees; but, as he spent most of his time up a tree or down a rabbit-hole, this would have been superfluous. He had entrancing, if over-ambitious, ideas for the future of the Troop, was quick at fashoning all manner of things—from a snare to a mouse-trap—and could tell you all you wanted to know about birds and their habits. He had plaited a wonderful belt out of leather bootlaces, and his Scout staff was a mass of intricate carved designs. Jimmy was born to be a Boy Scout.

When I was first privileged to see the little book there were but six names inscribed therein; but they seemed to me in each case to carry descriptions very true to the originals, and the whole idea did more than anything else to convince me that the little lady had got at the spirit of Scouting from the start.

To her the six boys were intimate character studies, and she realised that the success of the venture must be built upon the information so gained. She had not for the moment any intention of herself becoming Scoutmaster to the 1st Bumblecombe, and her answer to Squid's tentative suggestion anent this summed up the question as far as she was concerned.

It was after one of their evening meetings at her house, and the boy had lingered behind the rest to inquire: "Please, miss, can a lady be a Scoutmaster?" And she had replied: "I don't know, Squid; I never thought about it. But if you are thinking of me, I *can* say that she won't. I'm sixty-two, Squid, and I have got quite enough to do already. Besides which, I should look absurd in a Scout hat, and I don't like getting my feet wet. No, I'll help you all I can, and nurse the Troop until a man comes along. And Squid," she added, "the 1st Bumblecombe is your own affair. *You* started the ball rolling; *you* made your own little home in the west; *you* collected the five spirits like unto yourself. And you will find as time goes on that there will arise situations with which only a man can deal, and that temptations come to you boys where only a man's guidance can avail. No, Squid, it's your show, not mine. Now you've got your Patrol, you've got to lead them. You can if you will; and at any rate, I'm relying on your help. You won't fail me?"

There was a slight pause, and then Squid had looked very straight into her eyes as he answered: "No, miss, I won't; none of us would do that. But I can't promise as they'll do what I tell them. They all want to do something different. It would be all right if we had a Scoutmaster, miss."

"I know," she replied, "and you are going to have one, too. But they don't grow on every bush, Squid; and as far as I can see they are rather difficult people to find—that is, the right sort. Meanwhile, you are Patrol Leader—boss of the show. You have always led in and out of school; and, as far as I know, you have led well. Do the same now, Squid. Be keen on your job; pass your Tests before anyone else; and, above all, think of the Scout Law as a real law of the Scouts, and of your good turns as your first job in life. The other fellows will follow if they see you mean business; and when your Scoutmaster comes along, he will want all the help you can give him."

"He shall have it, miss," said Squid, and, saluting, went home.

6

In her relations to the Owl Patrol Miss Simpkins had now reached a stage where she felt herself to be rather up a tree—metaphorically, of course. She did not attempt to emulate Jimmy Cape in this form of activity.

It would be true to say that, up to a point, the twice-weekly meetings at "The Shrubbery" had been at least as successful as could be expected. The thought of the amount of knowledge which she herself had assimilated during those early efforts sometimes brought a smile to her face, especially as she could not conceive what good the tying of sundry knots and the tracing of mystic signs could be to an old lady of sixty-two.

She realised, however, that if she was to be of any use to the boys, she had to answer their refreshing keenness with a knowledge of essentials at least thorough, if little more advanced, than their own.

I cannot think what the Rector would have said if he had seen the lady's occupation a few hours before the first meeting took place. Surrounded by odd pieces of rope, and with a broomstick across the arm-chair in front of her, she wrestled with the intricacies of the clove hitch. A Union Jack had taken the place of the antimacassar on the sofa, and the table was littered with sheets of paper covered with pencilled signs and compasses.

The result of all this endeavour had borne fruit in the comparative ease with which the boys had learnt the Tenderfoot Tests. Six weeks from the start they were all ready to take the Promise which would make them Scouts—even Tubby, to whom the accomplishment of a bowline had been such a terrible trial.

And then one evening Grainger had come over from the town to hold the first investiture of the Bumblecombe Troop.

The Rector and the boys' parents had been invited to the little ceremony. The former had pleaded the preparation of a sermon, but the parents turned up in force and crowded the small room to its utmost capacity. In spite of the crush, I have every reason for believing that the proper atmosphere was there; for the boys were on their best behaviour, even Buster forbearing to giggle when Sam, asked if he knew what his honour was, got as far as, "Yes, it means——" and then stuck hopelessly until prompted; and this, too, after betting anybody anything that he wouldn't be nervous.

Then there had been tea, dutiful Scouts waiting on their elders; and afterwards, when the visitors had gone, a little gathering round the fire and a few words from the Fairy Godmother.

"Well, boys," she had said, "you are real Scouts at last, and you've worked hard for it. You have won your spurs, as the old knights used to say; and now it's up to you to keep them bright."

And then she had told them simply, but with much power of imagination, the story of the young knight who had fared forth strong in the dignity of his new spurs and fired with the vows which he had just taken—fared forth on life's journey to fight evil wherever he should find it, and determined to spread the message of true chivalry in a world given over to selfishness; of how he had found Evil barring his progress at every step; and how that finally, by the help of God, remembrance of his promise, and pride in his symbol of honour, he had won through, and found that happiness which good deeds bravely wrought bring in their train.

"You are young knights, boys," she had said in conclusion, "for what is our Scout Brotherhood if not an Order of Chivalry? You, too, are going out into the world, and will sooner or later have to face evil and temptation. When they come I believe that the promise which you have taken to-day and the thought of the uniform which you now wear will help you, too, to win through. Remember those good turns. Wherever you look in your daily life you will find little kindnesses waiting to be done, little acts of knightly chivalry which make the world so much the brighter for those around you. Accept the experience of an old woman who, if she may say so, has learnt happiness through service for others."

The boys had been unusually silent on the way home that night, and Jimmy's comment—" better nor any of parson's sermons "—was accepted as the general verdict, while Squid's remark at parting, that anyhow the 1st Bumblecombe had got to be the " best Troop ever," found, I truly believe, an echo in five young hearts.

All this was very nice, and quite as it should be ; but it did not do anything to solve the problem of a Scoutmaster. One or two names had occurred from time to time to Miss Simpkins, only to be dismissed as unsuitable on riper reflection.

There were the two Whatleys, for instance—excellent young fellows of twenty-two and four respectively—good solid farming stock, and with leisure in the evenings, but with about as much imagination as the average rabbit. Mr. Paul, the schoolmaster, might have done if he had not been out of sympathy with boys generally. Young Vicars, who kept the garage and humoured the Ford, was a distinct possibility until his one assistant left the parish and left him single-handed.

Jack Boden was the one man who stood out above all the others as likely to be just what was wanted. He was the son of old Boden, the present Rector's immediate predecessor, and a cousin of Miss Simpkins herself. But Jack was for the present occupied with other things and said that he could not be bothered.

Since his father's death he had been many things in

many lands. Left with enough to keep him, he had spent the first fifteen years after coming down from Oxford in an assortment of ways, which had given him a broad outlook, an independent spirit, a love of sport and the life of the great outdoors, and an understanding of his fellow-man.

He had grown tea in Ceylon, ranched in Canada, shot big game in three continents, and served his country in the South African War; and now, at the ripe age of thirty-seven, had returned to Bumblecombe, bought a farm of some fifty acres, and proposed devoting himself to the breeding of pigs.

Jack Boden was a good fellow; all his friends—and he had many—were wont to declare that he was one of the best. Moreover, in his cousin's eyes, he was the ideal Scoutmaster, the natural leader of boys and men, with the gift of tact, the straightness of purpose, and the power of imagination brought to the surface by work and sport in wild places.

But she was not one to force the issue unduly, because she felt that Scouting was too big a thing to be taken up lightly. Jack was going to be Scoutmaster of the 1st Bumblecombe. The more she thought of him in this capacity, the more determined she was on that score. But she knew, none better, the advantage of the willing man over him who is pressed; and he should be allowed full time to grasp the meaning and possibilities of the new game. He should learn the simple directness of its appeal, and for himself find out that here was a means at hand, given in full measure only to the few, of leading in a game good for men and boys and for the country.

But for the present there were his pigs; and pigs, as we all know, are absorbing creatures.

He had met her first advance with a prompt statement of this fact.

"My dear Clara," he had said, "I've got all I want to do for the present. I don't know much about pigs yet; absolutely nothing about boys. And I don't suppose that the same treatment would suit 'em both. I must learn one thing at a time. At present it's pigs, pigs, pigs. When I've learnt all there is to know about those fascinating animals it will be time to think of light recreation. So leave me alone, there's a dear. Just look at that sow over there! Isn't she a beauty?"

So Miss Simpkins had wisely decided not to press the matter, but to work for her end through the art of subtle suggestion, or, as the Scouts would have it, on the principle of "softly, softly, catchee monkey!"

She opened her campaign by recommending Jimmy Cape for the office of deputy assistant keeper of the pigs. It was really most fortunate that the post happened to fall vacant just at the time, and still more fortunate that such a boy as Jimmy was there to fill it, combining as he did some small practical knowledge of the animals with a will to work and a red-hot enthusiasm for Scouting. Work at the farm ceased as a rule at 6 p.m., but he was in the habit of taking a last look round the stys before going to bed; and it therefore happened that twice a week a Scout uniform passed across the yard in front of Boden's study window.

In the matter of the predestined Scoutmaster there was also a staunch ally in the person of Lister, the doctor. Lister was a great believer in Scouts, and if it had not been for his professional duties and the weird hours attaching thereto, he might have become Scoutmaster himself. As it was, he gave up one hour a week to teaching the boys first-aid, and when they were fairly forward in its rudiments would occasionally accompany them on a Saturday afternoon ramble, and would devise strange and thrilling accidents on the spur of the moment to test their progress.

He was wont to relate these incidents to Boden when he went up to the farm for an evening pipe, but he never urged the subject of a Scoutmaster on such occasions. He believed with Miss Simpkins that it was merely a question of time; for he knew Jack, and, knowing him, foresaw that here, at any rate, seed well sown would fall on fruitful ground.

7

We now enter upon the last scene in the early days of the 1st Bumblecombe. With most Troops, I take it, even during the first years in the history of the Movement, the initial effort was that of the Scoutmaster collecting and training his boys. In Bumblecombe this procedure was reversed, and it was a case of the boys collecting and (shall we say ?) training their Scoutmaster.

Whatever the manner of it, few will disagree with the latter-day discovery that we older men can learn something from the boys whom it is our privilege to train.

We on our part give them happy employment, the fun and adventure of camp or trek, a helping hand out into the world.

But do not they give us something in return ? To the jaded, a fresh outlook on life born of their own enthusiasm ; to the old, a new youth, mental if not bodily ; to the sceptic, a hope of better things bred of their natural optimism ; to the self-centred, a chance to break away from self and look beyond.

Even Miss Simpkins, most unselfish and devoted of women, confessed that the Owl Patrol had taught her many things quite unconnected with knots and secret signs. No woman, possessed as she was of an intelligence above the ordinary, can live all her days buried in a Bumblecombe without occasionally finding the need for something wider, something more free from rural convention. To those who busy themselves with good works there is always the danger of controlling a monopoly and of getting into the habit of feeling that they are essential to their fellows—a sort of human *sine qua non*—which is a state of mind generally mistaken and good for nobody.

Squid and his merry men had broken unconsciously, but

none the less rudely, into all that. They had taught her in the first place that it was actually possible to inaugurate an institution in her village without her help. That this help was eventually called in did not affect the point.

At sixty-two she had begun to consider herself an old woman, until the companionship of the boys had seriously threatened the idea. Looking back over her past history in regard to Bumblecombe, she now saw that she had been prone to think of the children as perhaps of secondary importance in comparison with her Church Guild, her Foreign Missions and her Mothers' Union.

Scouting had opened up a wider vision. The boys' keenness, their lively imagination, their innate chivalry towards herself, and their eagerness to learn all the rules of the new game had shown her, as nothing else could have done, that she could no longer be everything to everybody. Indeed, I should not be surprised to hear that there were even times when their very evident, if unexpressed, affection for herself made her wish that it was in her to give them all that a man could give. If she ever entertained such a thought, it was never openly expressed; but possibly it found an outlet in the unobtrusive but persistent attack which she was engaged in waging against Jack Boden's defences.

That he surrendered in the end was a matter of course—most people did when Miss Simpkins was on the opposing side.

The assault was opened, as we have seen, by the introduction of Jimmy Cape into the sanctity of the pig-farm. This initial advance was followed up by a presentation copy of *Scouting for Boys*, with an intimation that when he had exhausted all the available literature on the subject of pigs, he might care to peruse one of the most human books ever written; and, like a wise woman, she drew particular attention to those pages which deal with camping, Nature study, and life in the open generally.

Up to this point there had been no attempt at counter-attack on Jack's part ; but one was seriously threatened when he found himself appointed sole examiner for the Farmer, Naturalist, Cyclist, Horseman and Blacksmith Badges.

It was undoubtedly a dispensation of Providence that he should descend from his farm to remonstrate in person upon the very evening and at the self-same hour as that appointed by the doctor for the examination of his class in the Second Class Ambulance Test.

It is difficult to maintain a dignified enmity when one is received with open arms by the foe and a cheery salute from six boys, two of whom are lying bandaged upon the floor ; nor even was it possible to plead the necessity for looking after his pigs, and thereupon retire in good order ; for was not that Jimmy Cape's face grinning up at him from the hearthrug, as far as the appropriate bandage for a scalp-wound would allow ? And Jimmy knew perfectly well that the pigs would be quite happy and contented until six o'clock the next morning.

There was, in fact, nothing to be done but to accept with a good grace an invitation to come in and help as official referee, and to see that the candidates were not passed too easily.

He could not have been expected, however, to foresee the still further consolidation of Cousin Clara's position by her announcement, after the bandages had been neatly folded up and put away, that the fire should be stoked up, and then they would all gather round and listen to some of Mr. Boden's yarns. The applause which greeted her words was too sincere to brook of any refusal, and so he sat himself down in the middle of a charmed circle and yarned to those boys for a solid hour. What is more, he thoroughly enjoyed doing it, for Jack was a good talker, and had an ample store of exciting experiences upon which to draw.

After it was all over he was fain to admit that he had never had a better audience.

"Well, Clara," he said, when the door had closed behind the last of them, "I congratulate you on your Boy Scouts; they are a jolly little lot. I came here to quarrel with you about that badge business, but I'm blest if I can now. I'll examine any of the young beggars you care to send up."

The lady's reply was typical of her:

"That's all right, Jack. But, as a matter of fact, they are not *my* Boy Scouts. I'm merely looking after them until your horizon ceases to be bounded entirely by pigs. It's your job, and you know it."

"My dearest woman," retorted Jack, "we've had all this out before. Some day possibly, but not now. There are few things I wouldn't do for you, Clara; but for the present the pigs——"

"For Heaven's sake spare me the pigs, Jack!" wailed Miss Simpkins. "There is only one thing I would suggest, before we close this painful interview, and that is that pigs need no character training; boys do. The destiny of a pig is to become bacon; that of a boy to become a man. However nice you are to your pigs, they will never look up to you as their natural leader, but merely as the bearer of the wash-pail, the harbinger of sharps. But you have much more than sharps to give these lads, Jack. Firm discipline, sympathy, encouragement in their budding hopes, the wide outlook, a love of Nature and of all God's beauty round us. Just think what you could teach them in camp! And, Jack, you were never self-centred, and they will keep you from the danger of ever becoming so. It's a man's work, this job of Scoutmaster, but it isn't given to every man to do it as you could. Go home, and forget your pigs."

Jack went home, but with every intention of forgetting Clara's boys. Somehow, though, they refused to fade from his memory. How keen they were! What a lot of young backwoodsmen he could make of them! Well—some day perhaps!

But the " some day " came sooner than was expected, and who shall say that Fate did not again intervene ?

It was on this wise. One Saturday afternoon the Owls were out on the trail. They had been following a track left conveniently in the mud by the resourceful Jimmy, and, feeling the need of a rest, had seated themselves upon a pile of stones at the foot of Harting Hill.

Now it happened that Jack Boden had recently acquired a motor-bicycle, and, not being very proficient in its handling, chose that precise moment to descend the hill much too fast, skid violently in trying to negotiate the bend at the bottom, and collapse with a crash in the hedge.

It was a matter of mere seconds before he was surrounded by the boys, who tried hard to hide their disappointment on being informed that he was unhurt.

" No, Squid, I'm sorry to say that I'm in no need of first-aid. If only the poor old bike wasn't smashed, I should feel bound to go up to the top and do it again, if only to give you fellows a chance to tie me up."

Up to now he had remained sitting in the hedge where he had fallen, and it was only the effort of rising that showed that something was amiss. He sat down again abruptly with a white face and a wry smile.

" Squid, you're in luck after all—left ankle gone. Know what to do ? "

He was left in little doubt on that score, and but a few minutes sufficed to see a solemn procession setting off for the farm, Jack borne tenderly but triumphantly on an improvised stretcher, followed by two Scouts wheeling the author of his mishap.

I need not go into the full details of his convalescence ; the regret of Lister, not unmixed with delight at his pupil's treatment of their first real accident, or Clara Simpkins's comment : " Now, Jack, could your pigs have done that ? "

Rather let me pass on to the direct sequel, which took place one evening a week later.

Jimmy had announced that some of the Scouts would like to come and see how he was getting on, and it was under the disguise of polite inquiry after his precious ankle that the deputation was ushered in. Formal inquiries over, they came to business with the candour of boys.

"Please, Mr. Boden," said Squid the leader, "we want to know if you'll be our Scoutmaster?"

There, it was out at last, the question which had been the result of so much anxious thought on the part of the Owl Patrol.

Jack grinned. "You young rascals!" he answered. "So that's the game, is it? You know perfectly well that I can't run away. But how do you know that I should make a good Scoutmaster? It will take some doing to live up to you fellows."

"Oh, we'll all help you, sir," quoth Buster.

Jack smiled. "I really believe you will," he said. "Anyhow, I accept." He looked round on their eager faces, and his own caught something of their eagerness as he continued: "And I shall be very proud to be Scoutmaster of the 1st Bumblecombe."

And so the matter was settled to the mutual satisfaction of all concerned.

Nor did Jack, having once taken the plunge, look back. As instance of this, I may quote from a letter written by him a year later to his old friend, Geoffrey Tindal, in far-away Manitoba.

"You know Geoff," ran the extract, "that I became a Scoutmaster just a year ago. You are always asking tenderly after my pigs, but never after my Scouts. There are twenty-four of them (Scouts, not pigs), and we are a very happy family. You remember the old days away in the Rockies—what times we two had together—hunting, prospecting, sometimes quarrelling, what not?

" Well, Geoff, these boys bring those times back to me ; and when we hit the trail of a Saturday afternoon, or sit round a log blaze with the moon shredding the pool below, and call up the owls all round, it still begets in me that humble feeling we both often felt out there. But with it now there is a deep thankfulness that I learnt something of what Nature can teach us, and that I am privileged to hand it on to a handful of youngsters.

" It's a great game, this Scouting, Geoff ; but it's a man's job all right—a game where one can help a Tenderfoot over some of the pitfalls. When you come home next fall, you must come down here. You shall camp with us, yarn to us, follow the spoor of the wily otter to your heart's content ; and perhaps—who knows ?—learn something of the fascination of Scouting. There are disappointments in it, but never disillusions. I used to think, when things went wrong, that it was the boys, then perhaps the game ; but I always came to see in the end that it was the Scoutmaster, and my pride has had many a fall in consequence—in fact, I am learning in my old age, Geoff, that there is great happiness as well as much fun in this game with the youngsters. I loved the life out there with you, old son—the shooting, the fishing, and sometimes, when we felt inclined, the work—but now for me it is England, pigs, and a Troop of merry Scouts ; and not for the world would I have it otherwise."

IV

THE VILLAGE OF EVERGREEN

I

THE month was June, the hour was eleven-thirty, and Markham Heslet was laboriously peddling a dilapidated bicycle up a long but well-graded slope.

There were indications that he would presently gain the top, and his map had informed him some time previously that the name of this particular hill was Sedgwick End.

Quite a nice name as names go, he thought; but it occurred to him at the moment that " Markham End " would be more appropriate; for he had been on the move since ten o'clock, and there was not the faintest breeze to temper the sun's rays.

Back there in the wilds from which he had recently returned Heslet had been heard to declare more than once that, as far as he was concerned, the sun need never shine again. And yet, on this cloudless, breathless morning, toiling at an unaccustomed exercise, he was none the less happy and care-free, and inclined to be very content with things as he found them.

For, afterall, this was England, and—well, one didn't mind the sun in England.

Here it was more of the shy maid than the raucous bully. It shone upon greens and greys and rich russet-browns; and there was nothing of the callous, unwinking glare upon naked sand or salt-pan, which made of it as much a foe to be feared as a friend to be welcomed in that desert country where the most fruitful years of his life had been spent.

Presently he breasted the last little pitch, and the going became easier, so that he was able to take more note of the landscape on either hand; and he concluded that without doubt the arduous climb had been worth while.

The road here and for a straight mile ahead ran along a hogsback between twin valleys; and to right and left of him the country fell away in gently undulating slopes of young corn, varied by many a coppice, hedgerow, or vivid patch of grass land.

Little red-roofed farms and cottages, and across the valley on his left a stumpy grey church tower, added to the peace and plenty of the scene.

To eyes more used to the blazing monotony of an eastern desert it was a feast of colour indeed. The gold of buttercups, the fresh green of meadow grass, the darker hue of massed trees or shady hollow and, far beyond, the faint blue line of the Cotswolds, all brought their share to his willing sight, as if they too would bid him welcome to his own land.

As he free-wheeled down a welcome dip with a momentum which just took him to the top of the opposite rise, he was thinking with some amusement of a conversation which had absorbed the attention of his companions of the smoking-room one evening during the homeward voyage.

The ship had passed through the Straits of Messina that afternoon, and from early morning onwards the great white cone of Etna had hung aloof and beautiful between blue sky and bluer sea away to the west.

Many of them had passed that way more than once, but few had had the good-fortune to see the great volcano under such perfect conditions. The sight had been the means of starting a lively discussion as to what in the experience of each was the most beautiful thing in the way of natural scenery he had yet encountered.

The whole world, from Fiji to the Grand Cañon, had been passed in review that evening; and when old Colonel Slater had turned to him with the words, " Come on, Heslet, let's hear your opinion; you have seen as much of the jolly old globe as most of us," he had caused some surprise by his quiet reply: " What about the heart of England on a summer morning ? "

And so, as he rode slowly along he was thinking to himself that they might buck as much as they liked about such things as the Himalayas from Simla, sunset over the trackless desert, or the marvels of Sydney Harbour. They could romance to their hearts' content about the buried cities of the Incas, the temples of ancient Egypt, or the Italian lakes. Many of these he himself had seen and admired, for he had been a wanderer in far places all his life. He, too, had walked amongst the crumbling stones of ruined temples, and had watched—more times than he cared to remember—the eastern sun go down in a blaze of orange and scarlet behind the rim of the desert.

Few men had probably seen more of Nature's grandest and most awe-inspiring moments than Heslet. But with it all he had returned to England on his infrequent periods of well-earned leave with the feeling that, for him, the best experience of any was that of getting back to his own country of wooded hills and shallow valleys, of snug, contented fields, little brooks and soft grey skies, of trim hedges and splendid trees, of nestling farms and homely cottages.

And most typical of all that is best in English scenery, he thought, was that which lay spread at his feet when an hour later the road took a sharp turn before beginning its steep descent from the bluff point of Sedgwick End.

For down below him, at a point where the two valleys met and became one, lay a delightful jumble of half-timbered and cream-washed cottages with thatched roofs and gay gardens, dominated by the squat tower of a little Norman church, and soothed to slumber by the placid, gently flowing waters of the Sedge.

Heslet dismounted from his bicycle, opened out his map, and, with some difficulty, identified the village as Evergreen.

It was surely the very heart of England which beat here, he thought, as he let his machine subside into a bed of bracken, and sat himself down beneath the welcome shade of a group of silver-birch trees.

For some time he had had suspicions of his back tyre, and he now noticed that it was quite flat. But this fact did not worry him unduly—he was going no farther that morning if he could help it, and no doubt Evergreen, for all its rusticity, possessed some sort of a shop where the machine could be repaired. There would also be an inn where he could get something to eat; and as his time was his own, there was really no particular need for hurry.

So he lay back in the deep bracken, mopped his brow, and looked at his watch; and presently the bells of the little church below chimed out and announced that it was noon, and indeed high time for a weary traveller to seek the shelter of the village inn.

He was beginning idly to picture that inn to himself. To be in keeping with the rest, he decided, it should be half-timbered, gabled and mellow, panelled wainscot and ancient oak within, and with a battered sign swinging above the door, a nice garden and a bowling-green—just as it should be. And he yawned prodigiously and closed his eyes, and might even have slept had it not been that a slight noise caused him to raise his head above the bracken and look round, to meet the level gaze of a small boy clad in the familiar uniform of a Scout, who had just dismounted from a much smarter machine than his own.

The boy looked at Heslet, and Heslet looked at the boy; and the boy finally fixed his gaze on the flat tyre.

"Hullo!" said Heslet. "Bit of a crock, isn't it?"

The youngster considered him gravely for a moment, as if summing him up for a definite purpose, and then turned again to the main object of interest.

" Back tyre's flat," he remarked. " I'll mend it."

Heslet looked at him doubtfully, and hesitated. He was not sure that he wanted the operation performed so far from the village inn, as it would mean foregoing a well-earned lunch for at least twenty minutes.

On the other hand, he felt that a refusal would deprive the young man of a golden opportunity for doing his good turn, and such chances might be rare in the village of Evergreen.

Heslet was good-natured, and at any rate the matter would bear argument, and so he said : " It's very good of you, but the village is only half a mile away, and I suppose there is a garage of sorts there."

While he was speaking the boy had commenced to unstrap the wallet at the back of his saddle, and any chance of an early lunch appeared to be fast slipping away. But he looked up and nodded thoughtfully.

" There be Joe Snippet," he conceded. " 'Tisn't hardly a garage, but he mends bikes and sells petrol " ; and then a smile of inspiration illumined his face as he glanced at his wrist-watch and added : " Maybe he'll be gone to his dinner now."

Heslet replied that he was in no hurry for the tyre to be mended ; he would walk down to the village and await Joe Snippet's return from dinner with equanimity as long as he could get some for himself.

He thought that he had checkmated his young friend there, but the boy was still undefeated.

" I want to get my Cyclist Badge," he explained ; " and Mr. Cartright he told me as I must mend a puncture on the road all alone, and prove I done it. So if I mend yourn and you give me a note to Mr. Cartright to say as how I done it all right, I expect he'll pass that."

Heslet still hesitated. But when the youngster pleaded, " Let me mend it, sir ; won't take more'n ten minutes," he recognised his position as untenable, and gave in with an outward good grace but an inward sigh.

"Righto!" he said. "Carry on. Besides, it will be your good turn for the day, wont' it?"

The reply to this was unexpected and rather crushing.

"Did that at half-past six this morning!" And then, "My word, this be a rotten cover! Won't last you long, sir. Joe Snippet he sells covers. Better get a new one from him if you be goin' far."

He administered his mixture of reproof and advice while in the act of removing the cover from the rusty rim, and the job appeared to require so much care that Heslet offered to help; but this was declined with dignity.

"Mr. Cartright he says as how I've got to do it all myself." So there was nothing for it but to recline once more on the soft bracken and play the rôle of a mere onlooker, with a thirst not only for cider but for general information.

"How old are you?" Heslet asked.

The boy replied without looking up: "Fourteen come August, sir."

"Been a Scout long?"

"Nigh two years."

"Mr. Cartright your Scoutmaster, I suppose?"

"He be that."

By this time the operation of removing the cover was safely accomplished, and the boy suggested the shifting of the whole show to a wayside pool some fifty yards farther back.

He allowed Heslet to help in doing this, and also in the subsequent proceedings, which necessitated the holding of his ancient bicycle bodily over the surface of the water while the half-inflated tube was held under for the purpose of diagnosis.

It was a most precarious position; one slip and the whole show, Heslet and all, would have disappeared into unknown depths of muddy water. Not that he would have minded much about the bicycle—he was beginning to dislike it—but he was distinctly anxious about his only suit of clothes.

He felt rather like the anæsthetist at a critical operation, with the small Scout in the rôle of an eminent surgeon dabbling his fingers in the blood (or perhaps mud) of his victim; and his arms were beginning to ache abominably when the boy looked up with a bright smile and indicated with a muddy forefinger four rows of small bubbles.

"Fair sieve she be, sir. Got a pencil?"

Heslet produced the required article, and one by one the holes were located and marked.

This done he was permitted to stand the machine upside down on the ground, while the boy removed his scarf and dried the inner tube therewith. It was a nice scarf of russet-brown; and Heslet, considering its misuse in this way in the light of a singular act of self-sacrifice, felt bound to make a remark to that effect. But he was informed that it really did not matter at all.

"Mr. Cartright he says as our uniform is meant to be used, and not put away wi' lavender. Besides, it'll wash." So that was that.

But the reply left him with a desire to meet this Mr. Cartright, who appeared to occupy such a prominent position in the thoughts of his young friend. So he ventured to express a hope that before long he would have an opportunity of making Mr. Cartright's acquaintance.

"Oh, that should be easy, sir," the boy replied, intent upon gumming the patches—"leastways if you aren't in no hurry. Likely he'll be in camp by five o'clock. Always gets to camp by then."

Heslet considered this fresh piece of information for a moment. It would, of course, mean stopping the night at the village inn; but, as the idea of so doing had already occurred to his mind, he decided there and then to act upon it.

There were reasons, when he came to think of it, why he *should* stop the night in Evergreen. There was the necessity of fitting a new cover for one thing—not that it would take very long to do that; also, as far as he could see from his present point of vantage, the village was surrounded by hills, which meant that he would have to face another long climb on leaving it; and it was very hot.

But perhaps the reason which weighed most with him was the attractiveness of the little place itself—one of those spots which bid one stop, and rest, and dream the hours away.

He turned to the boy, therefore, with a smile. "So you have a camp here?" he queried.

"Why yes, sir," said the Scout. "We camp every week-end in the long meadow up Sedge Brook. 'Taint more than half a mile from the 'Three Crows.'"

By this time it appeared that the tyre would bear at least a partial inflation, and Heslet's services were again requisitioned to enable the tube to be tested under water; and the boy presently announced: "She'll do now; I'll put her back."

He put her back, and proceeded to inflate her; and presently there was a plump, healthy-looking back tyre once more.

"That's fine!" said Heslet; but the boy pinched the cover doubtfully.

"'Twill be, if so be as you gets to the inn on it all right," he said.

"Well," suggested the other, "you had better ride there with me; and, if all goes well, I'll write you out a certificate when we get there—all in ink on nice white paper, as it should be."

They mounted and rode slowly down the hill.

"By the way," asked Heslet, "what's your name?"

The boy looked rather surprised that his companion should not know this without the necessity of asking.

"Why, Harry Giles be my name," he said.

"Son of Farmer Giles, I imagine?" suggested Heslet.

He had no reason whatever for this assurance beyond the fact that it appeared inconceivable that there could be anyone of that name in the village of Evergreen who was not a farmer; and it was with a distinct feeling of relief that he received the reply, "I be that," as they dismounted at the door of the "Three Crows" and leant their bicycles against the wall near by; for it would have been something of a shock if the boy had announced that, on the contrary, his father was a dealer in wireless apparatus, or something equally out of keeping with half-timbering and thatch.

"Come along in, then," he said, "and we'll find a pen and a sheet of paper—also perhaps a bottle of cider. Just run along and find someone, will you?"

The boy departed down the little passage, and returned presently in company with the innkeeper himself, who was hastily wiping his large hands on a white apron, and whose genial countenance expressed interrogation.

"Harry and I," Heslet explained, "have been mending punctures in my rear tube for the last twenty minutes—at least Harry has, and I have been looking on. We are both hot and thirsty, and desire nothing so much as two mugs of your best cider, also a pen, some ink and a sheet of paper, so that I can persuade his Scoutmaster of his skill in mending punctures. Then I should like some lunch in your oak-panelled coffee-room—something cold and simple—and after lunch I propose to sit in the rose-garden overlooking your bowling-green to smoke a restful pipe while a bedroom is made ready for my night's lodging—that is to say, of course, if you have one available."

He paused for breath, while the big man beamed upon him.

"Why, sir, seems to me as how you've been here afore," he replied. "Leastways, you know all about the 'Three Crows.'"

It was Heslet's turn to show surprise.

"Don't tell me," he said, "that you really have all those delightful things—rose-gardens and oak-panelling? When I got my first glimpse of Evergreen from the hill yonder, I thought to myself that nothing short of an inn with oak-panelling would do, but the reality so often falls short of the ideal."

"Oh, it don't in Evergreen," the other retorted from behind the bar, where he was engaged in drawing two great mugs of cider. "Harry there might have told ye all that, specially him being a Scout; but maybe mending tyres don't go with old oak and rose-gardens. Anyhow, here be your cider; and what was it—pen, ink and paper you said? You shall have 'em at once, sir; and the lunch and the bedroom;" and he thereupon retreated to the back regions, calling lustily as he went for one Sarah.

2

When the two had sampled the cider to their satisfaction, Heslet wrote out a certificate in his best handwriting, folded it neatly and gave it to the boy; and then he asked him a few questions about Boy Scouts generaly, and about the little badges which the youngster was wlearing on the sleeves of his khaki shirt.

The boy answered eagerly, and was so evidently keen about it that Heslet got quite interested, and neither of them noticed the passage of time until Mr. Blackett, the host, came back to announce that his guest's lunch was ready.

During the meal Heslet continued his catechism on the subject with the innkeeper, who served him with his own hands.

"That boy seems keen on the Scouts," he said; and the other agreed.

"Keen, you say?" he replied. "Aye, he's keen enough; so be they all. 'Tis a fine thing, this Scouting, sir—a fine thing it be; teaches 'em sense and makes 'em nippy. Parson started 'em off, he did, when he first came, nigh three years back. Now we've got Scouts, and the little chaps—Wolf Cubs they calls 'em; and Rovers for the big 'uns; and Guides and Brownies for the girls. Why, I doubt me if every child in the village ain't in it one way or t'other soon almost as they can walk." Mr. Blackett broke into a chuckle as he continued: "And parson, he makes us all do something for 'em—parents' committees and such like. Why, sir, blessed if he didn't make me chairman, as they calls it; and Giles—that be Harry's father—he be secretary; and old Lumpas looks after the money—fancy old Lumpas looking after anything but hisself—but we was all like that till parson came, nigh three years back. And now, why, bless you, we be keen as the boys and girls theirselves. It be sure a wonderful thing—me at my age, too. We've got a meeting this very evening to arrange a whist drive for 'em, and it takes something good to get me out of the 'Three Crows' of a night. Try a bit of this Stilton, sir; it be good and ripe."

Heslet accepted the Stilton with a smile.

"If I stay long under your roof, Mr. Blackett, I shall be roped in, too," he replied. "Your parson seems to be one of the irresistible sort."

"Well, I don't hardly know as he's that, sir," said the innkeeper—"leastways he didn't worry us a big lot about it. But he had a meeting to talk it all over when he first came, and he made it seem somehow as if it was the only thing to do—without saying much, you know. Anyhow, he got what he wanted, and here we all are, in it up to our necks, so to speak, and," he added with a twinkle, "if so be as you meets him, sir, it wouldn't surprise me one bit to see you running about in a pair of bare knees and one o' them shirts inside of a week. But there, perhaps you are not goin' to stay; and, if I talks like this much more, maybe you won't. So, if you've finished I'll have my bit, and you can take your pipe out to the garden."

Mr. Blackett thereupon departed, and Heslet lit his pipe and went out through the back door.

Like many old inns the back view was even more attractive than the front, displaying a perfect riot of crooked gables and quaintly carved woodwork. He noticed that whereas modern windows of a convenient type had been put in to face the road, those looking on to the garden had the original leaded diamond panes.

Great masses of purple passion-flower and climbing roses covered the walls at intervals up to the very eaves, and the door through which he had just come was embellished at the lintel with two quaint little carved figures pointing inwards to the date 1605.

Heslet spent some time in examining the details of this gem of half-timbering, and then turned his attention to the roses.

Mr. Blackett evidently knew something about roses; and his garden, though small, was well worth the study of one whose ambition it had been for years to grow them himself when he had done with deserts and savages and irrigation schemes, and could settle down to a quiet old age in his own country.

Away back there he had often dreamed of the rest and peace of quiet pursuits, a little cottage in some nook of England far off the beaten track; and, of course, roses—a regular riot of them, like Blackett's here in Evergreen.

Heslet murmured the name softly as he sank into a deep wicker-chair, and turned it round so that he could get a glimpse of the old house above the many-coloured mass of blossom.

Why not Evergreen? He would have to go far, he thought to himself, before he found another place so near his ideal, so peaceful, so typically English.

It seemed to him, indeed, that not he, but a kindly Fate, had held the handlebars of his dilapidated machine that morning; for there had been no set purpose about his journey beyond that of the casual wanderer.

Six months of idleness in London, wandering about

from club to club looking up old friends, had stifled him. And so he had bought his crock, packed a rucksack with bare necessities, and, attired in his oldest and most friendly tweed garments, set out down the Oxford road with no idea of a definite destination. If he liked the look of a village, he would stop there. If wide road or leafy lane showed promise of further attraction, it should be followed.

There was a map in his pocket, of course, but that was merely for the purpose of discovering which particular part of England he had reached, and played no part in planning the day's itinerary.

And so he had come by devious ways to Evergreen, in the valley of the Sedge; and here he found himself sitting and smoking his pipe amidst surroundings charmed and mellowed by the centuries.

Markham Heslet leant back and closed his eyes, drinking deep into the soothing peace of this little old garden under the hill. The murmur of countless bees amongst the roses, the distant lowing of cattle, and the pleasant quarrelling of rooks in their high eyrie over his head mingled harmoniously with the deep, persistent hum of a threshing-machine up the valley. It is probable that this quiet medley of country sounds would have induced slumber, especially in view of those two noble tankards of Mr. Blackett's home-brewed cider, had it not been that there was much to occupy his mind.

He was, indeed, thinking hard as he lay back in his chair, and his thoughts mainly concerned themselves with the difficult problem of balancing the past with the future.

When he had finally shaken the acrid dust of the East from off his feet, moved on like many another to make room for enlightened native inefficiency, he had felt ill and prematurely old with the intolerable strain of giving his best in the service of those who could indeed pay, but were incapable of either appreciating or honouring the motives of the giver.

But now, after some months of rest in a white man's country, he was feeling as fit as he had ever felt in his life—fitter, indeed, than at any time during the last ten years.

Away out there—thwarted, disappointed, and at the last really not fit to cope with increasing worries—there was nothing he had longed for so much as the time when he could give it all up and retire to live the life of an Englishman in his own land.

But, now that the time had come, the affair took on another aspect.

Not that he regretted the decision which had built, as it were, a wall between him and his past career, and had finally sent him home with an adequate, if not over-generous, pension. But the lassitude, the disappointment, had gone; his strength and virility of mind had returned; and he could not help looking forward to the years ahead with a touch of doubt, almost of dismay.

Heslet had been an intense worker all his life—a constructive worker with a capacity for detail and a gift for handling those under him which many thought amounted to genius.

It was little wonder, therefore, that he was thinking on that June afternoon that the growing of roses, fascinating and difficult though it might be, would scarcely suffice to fill his life in the years to come.

Many were the ideas which flitted through his active brain as he lay apparently asleep, with his neglected pipe cold on the grass beside him.

The many forms of farming and commerce were all passed in review, weighed, and in some detail found wanting. For one thing, he considered that he had amply sufficient for his small needs; there was nobody dependent on him, and there was little reason, therefore, why he should attempt to win for himself what he could not spend.

But there was reason, he thought, why some means should be found for the continued exercise of such talents as he possessed, even though it should lie in a smaller and less exacting sphere.

Like all men of his type, he had a passionate, if deeply hidden, love for his country and kind, and it was natural, therefore, that any practical common-sense form of service to them should seem to be the possible solution of the difficulty.

If, indeed, Kismet had led him by the hand and found him Evergreen, was it too much to hope that she would continue her favours and point out the path before him? Was it too much to say that, in coming to this little village under the hill, already he might have found what he needed—the germ of an idea and the means by which it might be made to ripen?

Anyhow, a day or two would show, he thought. So he picked up his neglected pipe, put it in his pocket, and strolled back towards the inn, intending to see what manner of lodging had been prepared for him, and to warn Mr. Blackett of the possibility of an extended stay under his roof.

3

He had nearly reached the door when it was opened from within to disclose a small wiry person in clerical attire. In the immediate background stood Mr. Blackett, engaged in wiping away the remains of a final draught with the back of one hand.

"Ah, here he be, parson!" said the innkeeper, indicating Heslet; and the little clergyman stepped through the doorway and came forward with a pleasant smile of greeting.

"My name is Doughty—Canon Doughty—and I'm Vicar of this sleepy little backwater," he informed him; and then, as if in extenuation of his presence at the inn, went on to explain that he never lost an opportunity of smelling Blackett's roses.

"As a matter of fact, three reasons brought me here," he continued. "Mrs. Blackett, who is rather under the weather these days, the roses, and yourself. We don't see many visitors at Evergreen, and, being terrible gossips, get rather tired of each other's conversation. A visitor is a godsend, Mr. Heslet. You see, I know your name already. Harry Giles proudly showed me your certificate ; it was good of you to help him."

While he was talking he had gently led the other back down the garden to a small summer-house at the far end of the bowling-green. They had seated themselves, by mutual consent as it were, in two wicker-chairs.

" I think, rather, that it was Harry Giles who helped *me*," Heslet replied ; and the other smiled.

" I only hope, then, that he told you what he told me," he said.

" And what was that ? " Heslet asked.

" Only that ' it weren't really no blooming good mending that there tube, as it was fair rotten ! ' "

Heslet hastened to reassure him. " Harry was quite straight about it," he explained with a laugh. " He went so far as to give me the name of the local cycle dealer where I can get a new one. But he was so anxious to experiment that I hadn't the heart to refuse his help, and, after all, it saved me a half-mile walk."

Both men laughed.

" And incidentally brought Master Harry his certificate and a glass of cider," replied the Vicar. " But the boy is a keen Scout, and as nice a youngster as there is in the village. I needn't have doubted him telling you the worst."

" Seems very keen on his Scouting," Heslet commented—" in fact, we had quite a pow-wow on the subject."

Canon Doughty was engaged in drawing patterns with his stick in the gravel at his feet, and there was silence for a moment. Then he turned to his companion and said :

" Blackett tells me that you are thinking of stopping

here awhile, and that you seemed to be interested in the Scouts."

Heslet got his pipe well alight before he replied with a slight smile: "Interested? Well, if filling them up with cider and signing certificates betokens interest, I suppose that Blackett was right. I put a few idle questions, and he told me all about his own part in the show."

"He would," said the other. "And, after all, no one can help being interested to a certain extent, can he? It is my ambition, Mr. Heslet, that every child in the village shall have the chance of being a Scout or Guide. I came here from the East End, and in my experience there has never been anything which goes so far towards solving the problem of character training for young people as these two movements. It is the young people who are the fruitful soil for us parsons, you know. Not that their elders are necessarily stony or shallow—and I have had the privilege of helping a few elderly wanderers back to the straight path—but it is the boys and girls who matter most, after all. If we can start *them* right there will be fewer wanderers."

He paused to light a cigarette, and then went on: "I have seen very remarkable results from Scouting, Mr. Heslet. You see, it is the boys' own show—not merely something which we older people think is good for them, and thereafter heavily impress upon their reluctant souls—it's their very own; they love it. Start a Troop and watch 'em flock to join. There is something about it all—their keenness—which moves me very strongly. It is such a pathetic keenness when we think of the thousands of youngsters waiting a chance to play a game they love and which could mean so much to them—just waiting, asking to be led. I'm not boring you, I hope——"

Heslet shook his head. "Please go on."

And Canon Doughty continued: "Why, I met a boy, a stranger to the parish, as I was leaving camp yesterday. He was peeping at our lads through a hole in the fence when I came along. 'Hullo!' said I, 'you a Scout, too?' 'No such luck, sir,' he replied. 'All the lads in our village would join if there was a Troop; but parson he don't hold with Scouts.' If what he said is true, I could sit and watch that man boil, Mr. Heslet. Why, it's the greatest chance we parsons have ever had. As a class we don't study these organisations for young people as we should; we don't somehow get down to them enough. There are exceptions, of course, and magnificent work is being done here and there. But the youngsters should be our first care. Some of us are—well, to put it mildly, amazingly narrow."

"I dare say that is so," said Heslet; "but it seems to me that these same organisations (Scouts, Brigades and so on) give the layman his chance—perhaps his best opportunity, to the right man—for fitting into the scheme of things. I only wish I were twenty years younger. Fifty-eight and a bit of a liver are drawbacks, you know."

"I don't know about the liver, Mr. Heslet; never had one. But I'm fifty-five, and not too old at that to be young when I want to. After all, which is the leader these young people want—a boy possibly five years their senior, whose sole claim to authority lies in the fact that he can smack their heads and walks out with a girl, or the man who has seen a bit of the world, knocked up against some of the rocks, and thereafter marked 'em on his chart? Personally, I think that movements like the Scouts suffer too often from the youth and inexperience of those who run them—rather a case of the blind leading the blind. Give me the older man every time—the man who has handled men and conquered himself. He'll have the sympathy and understanding, even if his joints be stiffer than they were."

"I'm inclined to agree with you—at least in theory," Heslet answered. "But then I really know nothing about running a show like this.

"I've been abroad all my life, Vicar. They chucked me out at last, and I came home. At first I welcomed the idea of retirement, loafing, no responsibility, whatever name you like to put to it. Settled in London and looked up all the old cronies I could get to hear of. But it palled—bored me stiff in six months. You see, I had always lived in wild places and had to do with wild people who hadn't a liver among 'em.

"And so a week ago I bought a second-hand bike—I was had over the bargain if your Scout is to be believed—packed a few odds and ends into a rucksack, and set out to find the heart of England. Sounds poetic, doesn't it? But if you had spent the best years of your life at the very edge of beyond as I have, Vicar, you would understand better what I mean—the ache, the longing for all these things you have here in such abundance—lush meadows, quiet villages, old churches, the smell of wholesome rain, the peace and plenty of it all."

The Vicar nodded.

"I can quite understand all that," he said, "though I've not been much of a traveller myself. But we have our desert places here in England, you know—the parish I came from, for instance—except that there is nothing of the purity and freshness of the desert about it.

"I had the luck to be able to found a Mission for those poor dear people, Mr. Heslet—a little oasis in my desert. And, if my doctor had not insisted on a move, and gone to the bishop behind my back, I should be there still. Sometimes, in spite of them and my little breakdown, I feel that I was a bit of a coward to go—almost a deserter; that I ought to be back there among the appalling tenements, the overcrowding and the hopeless squalor of all."

He pulled a pipe from his pocket, carefully filled and lit it, and then went on: "We do what we can, of course, but it's an uphill job. I often wonder what people expect. They talk of Communism, red revolution—what not—and wonder vaguely how such things, if they come, will affect the even flow of their own comfortable lives. Very few of them have any idea of the conditions under which vast numbers of theii fellows live, and they don't take the trouble to find out.

"The fact is, they don't want to know—it's so much easier for their peace of mind not to. Take this Scout Movement, for example; it's a perfect godsend to the slum child, or would be if we could get enough men to run it. It's the most wonderful thing that has ever happened in education; but people don't realise it.

"They content themselves with a general approval fostered by the Press; they like to think that it may help to keep those dreadful Communists away for a bit longer; and they give a guinea perhaps now and again. But they leave the running of it to a few enthusiasts.

"It isn't entirely their fault, I suppose. It's the fault of what we call education. We concentrate on the three R's, and leave the responsibilities of birth, wealth, position, traditional leadership to find their way to the surface if and where they can. Thank God, they often do, but not enough—not nearly enough! And so you find Missions without adequate staffs—a vast field of happy and essential service to humanity with no takers. They simply don't know because they have never been told, and, above all, have never seen."

He took a tattered note-case from his pocket and handed a newspaper cutting to his companion. There was silence for a minute or two while Heslet read it through, broken only by the drone of bees and the distant sounds of the farmyard.

"I knew that boy," the Vicar went on as the other returned it to him—"a bright, cheery youngster, just like Harry Giles, full of spirits and courage—amazing courage. Father a drunkard, mother something worse; a family of eight living in one squalid room at the top of an eight-story tenement. Room! You could hardly dignify it by the name! Leaking roof, rotten floor, vice and vermin all round, and this lad running the show.

"Then they moved, and I lost sight of them. But the

sequel is fairly obvious. All that bright hope, struggle and grit—wonderful grit—dragged down, submerged, hopelessly warped. And the magistrate's comment, 'A pest to society.' Quite right, I suppose, according to the popular view. But what chance had the boy? What in the name of Christianity had society ever done for him? Educated him, I suppose—taught him to read and write—and then left him to fight impossible odds. We can imagine the rest—bad companionship, the craving for some relief from drudgery, temptation, and then these thefts; and now, eighteen months and the everlasting brand of the prison.

"Oh, I know all the difficulties. It's an immense problem, and I suppose that one is apt to judge harshly. But if you knew those people as I know them, Heslet—their pluck and humour and loyalty to each other—what a chance, what an opportunity for us who have known the good things of life—not for charity only, though, God knows, that is wanted—but for comradeship, a guiding hand, especially for the youngsters!"

He rose and stood for a moment looking up at the rooks which had just taken noisy possession of one of the neighbouring elms, and his gaze wandered from them to the trim garden, the mellow old house, the clear June sky beyond.

"That—and this," he continued softly. "All this beauty and peace and sweet cleanliness. I understand your longing for it away there in the desert; and you, I think, understand something of what I feel when I compare the two.

"It is wonderful! As you say, the heart of England. But there are spots which can be too restful, too easy, even too much blessed with God's goodness in Nature, when there is work to be done out there in the desert places."

Heslet nodded in comprehension, and the Vicar continued: "I shall go back when my strength is built up—back to the tenements, the squalor, and my poor under-staffed Mission——" And then he broke off suddenly with a little grimace as the church clock struck the hour, and faced his companion, watch in hand. "Four o'clock already. I don't know what you'll think of me taking up your afternoon like this; but I warned you that we are inveterate gossips down here, didn't I? Still, I'm sorry; it's hard to be a crank without being a bit of a bore too."

Heslet rose with a smile at the other's apology.

"If you have a crankiness, *padre*," he said, "it's not of the kind which bores. I think that you and I have much in common, and—well, I'm not so old but that I can still learn."

They walked the length of the bowling-green in silence, and then Heslet turned to the other and continued: "It might amuse you if I told you of old Blackett's prophecy, delivered with the Stilton at lunch to-day. The subject under discussion was the mystery surrounding the fact that three estimable and innocent villagers, such as himself, Giles, and Lumpas, should have been dragged in to take a hand with this Scouting business. He appears to have never quite fathomed the part that you played in it, and he went on to say that he wouldn't be surprised to see me running about in a pair of bare knees and a shirt after a brief acquaintance with 'parson.'"

He smiled whimsically. "After all, that would only be getting back to a kit which has served to hide my scragginess from the lizards and the snakes for many years past." He looked up at the crooked gables and back down the sunlit garden, and then turned to the Vicar with something of the eagerness of a boy.

"I tell you what it is, *padre*. I've fallen in love with your Evergreen, and I'm also in process of flirting with an idea. I think I'll stay here till I've worked it out. Who knows, I may yet have to send for those shorts. And now I'm going up to cadge a cup of tea off Harry. I want to meet the wonderful Mr. Cartright."

The Vicar led the way through the passage to the white road beyond.

"You will like Cartright," he said. "I wish that we had more like him. I should like to be able to staff St. Jude's with Cartrights. But come along; I'll pilot you as far as Slake Bridge, where you cross the Sedge, and then go about my business."

4

The two men passed out into the full glare of the sunlight and strolled slowly up the road.

Although past four o'clock, the afternoon was still quite hot enough to make hurrying almost an indecency, and there was also much in the way of quaint cottages and bright gardens to note on the way.

When they had almost reached the limits of the little street Heslet's eyes fell upon one cottage rather more dilapidated and delightful than the rest, which bore the sign "Evergreen Post Office" over the door.

Suddenly remembering that his rucksack would be hardly sufficient for a prolonged stay, he mumbled an excuse to his companion and turned in at the gate.

"Shorts?" queried the Vicar when he reappeared.

"I expect they'll arrive with the rest," replied Heslet. "I left all my stuff at my club, and have wired to the hall-porter to send it down."

"Good!" said the other. "If you really want to study the genus Scout, you could not have arrived at a more opportune moment. Some of the St. Jude's boys arrived yesterday to camp for a week with our lads down here. They come in relays from their slums all through the summer." He broke off with a chuckle, and then went on: "I had a bit of a fight to get the show going. They are dear good people, the Evergreen 'uns, Mr. Heslet, but they didn't like the idea of the pollution of their offspring, and we lost a few of our own Scouts for a time—until they made a wonderful discovery."

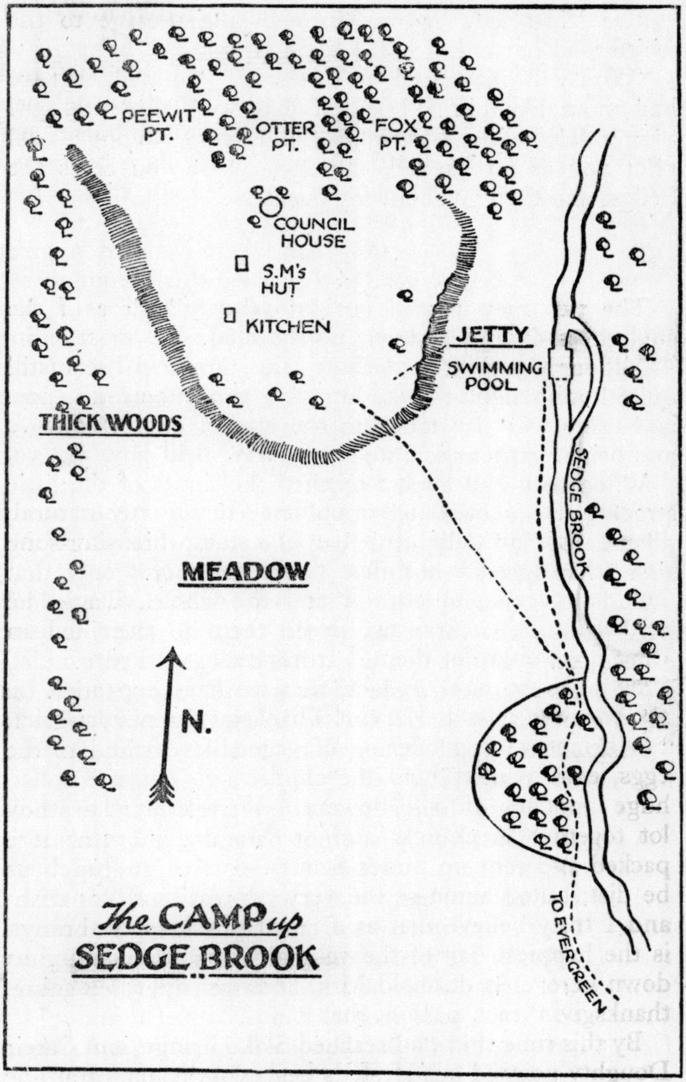
PEEWIT PT.
OTTER PT.
FOX PT.
COUNCIL HOUSE
S.M's HUT
KITCHEN
JETTY
SWIMMING POOL
THICK WOODS
SEDGE BROOK
MEADOW
N.
TO EVERGREEN
The CAMP up SEDGE BROOK

"That the pollution was more fancied than real?" suggested Heslet.

"Exactly; and also the truly remarkable fact that the apples and pears and plums still remained on their appointed trees, and not a single rick was burnt, nor were the gates left open—in short, the village continued the even tenor of its simple ways, except that a new interest had come into their lives.

"The first Sunday they were here we had a great Church Parade, and the whole village turned out to see them. I've never had such a congregation as I had that morning, Mr. Heslet; and perhaps the most telling thing about it was that those slum boys, in the matter of smartness and the way they wore their kit, gave points and a beating to the local braves."

"Good for them," said Heslet. "And how did you find the two lots mix in camp?"

"Bit shy of each other at first—that's only natural; but it was all right after the first camp-fire sing-song, and now they are the best of friends. Not only that, but the parents of our lot and the whole village look forward to their coming, invite them to their houses, can't do enough for them. It has really worked wonderfully well—so well, in fact, that we have expanded the scheme, and now at Harvest Thanksgiving everyone who can brings a little offering of vegetables, fruit, flowers, eggs, even poultry, and the children go out and collect huge bunches of wild-flowers. We gather the whole lot together in church, and on Monday morning it is packed and sent up under Scout escort to St. Jude's, to be distributed amongst the very poorest in that parish; and I truly believe that as a result our Harvest Festival is the happiest day of the year for our little community down here. As dear old Mrs. Dimmis says: 'It makes thanksgivin' reel, parson, that it do.'"

By this time they had reached Slake Bridge, and Canon Doughty pointed out Heslet's best route to the camp.

"You can't very well miss it," he added. "There

will be sounds of happiness to guide you. I hope to be up for the sing-song and a cup of cocoa later on. So long!"

Heslet sat for a few minutes on the coping of the old bridge to fill his pipe, and as he did so his eyes followed the retreating form of his late companion. He came to the conclusion that, just as he had liked the village at first sight, so also he liked its Vicar.

He began, in fact, to feel quite at home in Evergreen, and to consider that the wire to the hall-porter of his club had been a shilling well spent. For he had made up his mind to stay for awhile in this delightful spot, if only to see whether a closer acquaintance might persuade him to become a permanent resident thereof. He felt also that he would welcome a chance of learning something about the working of this Scout Movement.

He had always been attracted by the idea which lay behind, but the system which made the idea workable was still somewhat nebulous as far as he was concerned. This being so, he made up his mind, as he continued his walk in the direction of the "sounds of happiness," that he would pick up as much as he could from the Vicar, Cartright, and the boys themselves, especially from the boys.

Markham Heslet was one of those men who leave little to chance, and who depend upon critical personal observation to direct their movements. It could have been very truly said of him that he knew a good thing when he saw it, for he was a quick and accurate judge of both men and facts—a valuable trait in the character of one who had been obliged to carve a career out of unpromising material and to build his reputation—no mean one—upon a capacity for handling others.

Out at the back of beyond he had found it useful to approach both men and facts from a strictly critical point of view and to leave hearsay for personal proof. He was not one to be unduly swayed by popular sentiment, and he, like others, had watched the growth of this new Scouting idea with interest indeed, but an interest tempered by the suspicion that as a bubble it had arisen, so as a bubble it might dissolve once more into thin air.

The Vicar's eulogy had interested him more deeply than the other could have been aware while he was engaged in making it; for Heslet, with his instinctive knack of gauging the motives of others, had quickly decided that the *padre*, like himself, was not one to be satisfied with the surface appearance of things, but would probe below the surface amongst the roots and soil which gave them life.

As he left the welcome shade of an overgrown spinney and picked his way along a path beside the Sedge, there was one phrase the little man had used which returned to his mind. His companion had referred to Scouting as being "the boys' own movement"; and, if indeed this was so, it would prove, Heslet hoped and believed, to be the whole secret of its phenomenal success. In that case its rapid growth was sufficiently explained, and there need be no danger of an equally rapid deflation, nor even, he thought with a smile, of a gradual deterioration like that of his rear cycle tube so long as the supply of Cartright's and Harry Giles's held out.

Sauntering along with these thoughts for company, and puffing contentedly at his pipe, he presently entered the shadow of a thick coppice, through which the little river wound its way, half hidden by great clumps of bullrushes and osiers.

Following a path made difficult by usurping bramble-bushes and the lower branches of the thick-growing trees, he emerged at length into the sunlight once more, and at the same time found himself face to face with the second scene of his Scouting experience.

Some little distance from where he stood, the meadow, which had been gradually closing in between its wooded boundaries, reached its apex at the summit of a gentle slope of smooth turf dotted with clumps of bracken and a few firs.

The last fifty yards, before the meadow became finally merged in the surrounding woods, was apparently almost level, and this formed a little triangular plateau fifty feet or so above the Sedge.

Immediately below this plateau the river had been widened by means of a neatly constructed dam; the clay banks on either side had been cut square and revetted with short lengths of timber driven into the mud. The whole formed a very serviceable swimming-bath. In the centre floated a small raft, and at the far end was fixed a rustic diving stage.

Heslet knew something about the construction of dams, and his critical eye approved what he saw before him.

Half a dozen boys were splashing about or drying themselves on the bank, and he recognised his young friend of the morning about to take a header off the raft. The result was not altogether successful—rafts have a disconcerting way of tipping up—and Harry met the water with more resounding force than elegance.

" I shall have to gum some patches on *you*, young man, if you do that sort of thing," Heslet remarked, as the boy's head broke the surface with one hand held at the salute.

Harry grinned. " Do better'n that, sir," he spluttered, as he swam away to the diving stage. And his next effort was quite good, evoking a desire in his companions to show off their varied aquatic attainments.

Heslet watched and encouraged them for a few minutes, and then proceeded to examine the dam in more detail. Meanwhile the boys dried themselves, hastily got into their scanty clothes, and then quite naturally joined him, readily answering his interested questions.

" Well, it's a jolly good effort to build that all yourselves," he said. " Does you credit. Who thought it out—Mr. Cartright ? "

" Yes, sir," Harry answered. " It took us all last summer and winter to do, and we all did a bit—St. Jude's and ourselves."

"I see; and you had to divert the stream while you were building the dam, didn't you? That's the cutting over there. And, like wise people, you have kept it open in case of flood-water. Took a bit of doing, but well worth the trouble, eh?"

"Yes-sir," they agreed.

"Now I want to see your camp; and Harry can perhaps offer me a mug of tea in exchange for the cider—eh, Harry?"

The youngster grinned as he led the way up the slope to the little plateau.

Here Heslet had his first glimpse of the summer quarters of the Evergreen Scouts, and it was not quite what he had expected. There was no trim row of bell-tents, and he was hard put to it to discover where the boys slept until he noticed that the trees at this point receded to form three re-entrants, two natural and the third apparently cleared by hand.

Harry led the way to the nearest of these, and, as they entered it, pointed out a stout fir post rudely carved and painted and capped by a wooden effigy of a fox.

"This is the Fox Patrol camp," he explained, "and that's their hut," indicating a curious structure in the centre of the clearing.

Shaped like a ridge-pole tent, it consisted of two frames of larch-poles lashed together and interlocking at the top. Outside it was thatched like the cottages in the village, and the two ends were provided with curtains of sail-cloth, at this hour of the day fastened back to allow the air to pass through.

Across the clearing behind the hut stretched a clothes-line hung with a varied assortment of blankets, and down each side, close under the trees, there was quite a museum of camp-ovens, rudely made seats, and a weighing-machine of Heath Robinson aspect but practical utility, as Harry proceeded to demonstrate.

As he wandered around asking questions, Heslet was very interested in all the details of applied ingenuity, for there was something new to be seen in each of the little Patrol camps. All three had their appropriate totem poles, but the sleeping huts were slightly different in type, and the centre clearing contained in addition a large shelter made of thatch on a frame fixed some ten feet up the boles of three convenient firs.

"That's the Council House," Harry explained naïvely, and hastened to add: "but we have meals there when it's wet."

The Council House was furnished with a rough table and benches down one side, and in the centre there was an open fire-place consisting of a mill-stone let into the floor.

"That's the Council Fire," Harry went on, "where we have sing-songs sometimes and the Court-of-Honour meets."

"I see," said Heslet. "And those little tents over there—do you sleep in those too? Oh, the St. Jude's Scouts use those, do they? And what is that place over there where tea is being made?"

"That's the main kitchen, sir. You see, Mr. Cartright doesn't always allow us to cook in our own camps, and when we don't use them we do the cooking there; and Miss Lumpas comes up sometimes and teaches us to cook proper. She's the Cubmaster, too."

"And do the Wolf Cubs camp here with you?"

"No, sir," the boy replied, "not with us. But they are allowed to use the huts two week-ends, when the Scouts go trekking."

"Trekking, eh? And where do you trek to?"

"Well, you see, we pack what we want on the trek-cart—that's it over there—and then we go out and explore. Sometimes we don't know where we are goin' to camp the night—I expect Mr. Cartright knows, but he don't tell us—and sometimes he sends the Patrol Leaders to find a ground, and we go there."

"Do you like your Scouting, Harry?" queried Heslet.

The boy's eyes shone. "My word, yes! we all do," he replied. "And St. Jude's do, too—and they know a bit," he conceded gracefully.

At that moment there was a yell from the kitchen, "Kettle's boilin'!" and so their conversation was broken off for the more important matter of slabs of bread, generously spread with jam, and mugs of strong, hot tea.

5

During the little meal Heslet found no difficulty in making himself at home. He learnt the names, and the nicknames, of his young hosts, and was secretly surprised to find how easy they were to get on with.

They showed a delightful boyish courtesy towards their guest; the best log seat was covered with a potato-sack for his accommodation, the most appetising slice of bread-and-jam was specially selected for him, and Harry Giles insisted on giving up his own mug while he shared one with "Mousey" Smith, a sallow-faced youngster evidently from St. Jude's.

It was not difficult to tell the London boys from their country hosts, Heslet found. Apart from their rather undersized appearance generally, they usually showed greater readiness and intelligence in replying to his many questions.

Perhaps most of all it interested him to observe an absolute freedom from restraint in his presence and a refreshing lack of self-consciousness in their happy chatter. Apparently they accepted him entirely as one of themselves—one of the little family who inhabited their delightful plateau. They vied with each other in telling him all about their Troops and Patrols, and badges and cooking, and the Guides, who, they explained, had a camp of their own half-way up Sedgwick End.

"And the Rovers—them's the big lads—have their's at Blake's Farm," said one, known for obvious reasons as Ginger. "But they are away the week-end at Meltham, doin' a conference or somethin', and stayin' with the Meltham Rovers."

"That sounds nice and friendly," Heslet remarked, as he lit his pipe and gave a hand with the washing-up.

And presently a chance word by one of the boys led him on to tell them a yarn; and this first effort led to another and yet another, while the shadows lengthened and the big red sun began to disappear behind the bluff nose of Sedgwick End. And the boys sat enthralled.

Heslet was, in fact, thoroughly enjoying himself. He found their rapt attention and encouraging remarks of "Got another, sir?" at the end of each very stimulating; and had just completed an especial thriller, during the course of which his pipe had gone out for the sixth time, when a long-drawn-out "Camp aho . . . y!" came to their ears from the direction of the coppice beyond the swimming-pool, and they could make out a small party of Scouts coming out from the deep shade of the trees into the last red rays of the sun.

The newcomers were led by one whom Heslet took to be Cartright himself, and Harry presently assured him of the fact that it was indeed Mr. Cartright.

"Now at last I shall be able to make the acquaintance of your Scoutmaster," he replied with a smile, "and tell him how kind you have all been to me. I think I shall ask him to let me stay for the sing-song."

"And more stories, sir?" they demanded.

"Well, perhaps; but if so you've got to jolly well sing them out of me."

"That's all right, sir," quoth Ginger; "we'll turn Monkey on to sing 'Hiawatha.' He's a treat he is—ain't you, Monkey?"

Heslet could not help smiling at the aptness of the nickname as a small, sturdy boy with a tucked-up face grinned sheepishly and backed out of the limelight.

But at that moment Cartright and the rest came over the brow and up to the camp-fire.

The Scoutmaster of the Evergreen Troop was a big man, with the figure of an athlete well set off by his Scout kit. His hair was tinged with grey, and Heslet judged him to be about five-and-forty. He came forward with outstretched hand and a gay smile, professing much anxiety as to how his " young scamps " had been doing the honours of camp.

" First-rate," Heslet assured him. " But I haven't had time to see quite all the sights yet—tea intervened."

" Then you must come and have a look round before all the light goes," said the other. " What *have* you seen ? Patrol camps ? Swimming-pool, of course ? Council House ? Shower-bath ? Not seen our shower-bath ? Your education isn't complete until you've seen that. We are mighty proud of it." He led the way to a corner of the little plateau which Heslet had not yet explored.

At this point the ground fell away sharply in a smooth slope of turf, ending abruptly in a miniature sandstone cliff some fifteen feet in height. A neat fence had been built along the edge of this, and well-cut steps led down to a wooden jetty, which served to bridge the level ground below to within a few feet of the river.

The jetty was built on stout piers about eight feet high, and two things about it immediately drew Heslet's attention. One of these was a small iron tank within a yard of two of the river end, and the other a couple of upright spars carrying between them a long boom.

" A good old gyppy shadoof, by all that's holy ! " he exclaimed. " Where did you get the idea of that ? "

A rope and bucket was attached to the tip of the boom, and, as Cartright proceeded to demonstrate, the balance was so nicely adjusted that only the lightest effort was necessary to lift a full bucket neatly from the river and swing it without the loss of a drop to a position from which its contents could be emptied into the tank.

" Rather nice, isn't it ? " he replied. " I was at Alexandria for a few months during the War, and, being a bit of an engineer, spent some time in studying primitive methods of water-raising. Let's go down and see what happens."

So they descended to the level ground below by a ladder fixed to the staging, and here Heslet found very complete arrangements for washing. A bench provided with basins was fixed to the piers, and the floor beneath was of concrete with wooden battens, the whole being arranged to drain into a large box full of cinders, and thence into the river. Underneath the tank was a tap and rose, and the pulling of a cord operated the shower-bath.

"That's good!" said Heslet, when the shower had been tested to Cartright's satisfaction. "Not much excuse for being dirty in your camp, anyhow."

"No, there isn't," replied the other. "As a matter of fact, this shower business is a luxury. We don't really want it with the pool so close. But I like getting the boys to make all these things; it's all part of the game, and teaches them a lot about stresses, drainage, leverage, and especially, perhaps, how easy it is to do all sorts of things without complicated machinery. They love doing it, too, which is half the battle. Take that filter, for instance—quite simple and easily made, but not a vestige of soapsuds gets beyond it."

"Make the whole show themselves?" queried Heslet.

"Practically. A few of the fathers and big brothers came up and gave a hand. I was glad to have them for the heavier part of the work, and it made them all the keener on the Troop—in fact, it started the Rovers going."

"How on earth did you get all the timber?"

"Oh, there, of course, we were lucky. We couldn't possibly have bought it. But I happen to earn my daily bread by doing agent to my cousin, Johnnie Hitherington, who owns all this property.

"During the War the W.O. came along, cut down half of one of his pet larch plantations, and then discovered that they didn't really need it. Left the stuff lying about until after the Armistice, when Johnnie made them an offer to buy it back as it lay.

"You've met our one and only Vicar, I expect? Well, he went to Johnnie as soon as he heard of this, and talked to him like a father. Result: Johnnie sent for me, and I was able to tell him with a perfectly clear conscience that there was enough timber to supply all his needs in the way of hurdles, rails, and so on for years to come, and that the rest wouldn't fetch much owing to the cost of haulage, and that he might as well let the Scouts have as much as they wanted. Johnnie's a good sportsman—and he did.

"We built the dam, the huts, and the jetty, and have got enough over for our dream of the future—a real log hut. We made Johnnie Troop President on the strength of it."

Heslet laughed as he led the way down to the pool.

"Your Scouts are lucky young beggars," he said. "What a boy's paradise!"

"Yes, they are lucky, I suppose," Cartright replied. "But, hang it all, they're worth it—they are so jolly keen. I wish you had seen them sweating at that dam all through last summer and winter. Some of them slacked at times, of course, especially at first, but it wasn't popular. It became a regular tradition that slacking simply wasn't 'done' in the Evergreen Troop."

"Well, it's a good piece of work, that dam," said Heslet. "Dam's have been rather a speciality of mine. I like the way you've fixed that sluice."

"That wasn't our doing," interposed the other. "We had to get the local builder in for that, and the canal surveyor designed it. Wouldn't charge a penny either, and the builder only charged the bare cost of materials."

Heslet laughed.

"Canon Doughty again, I suppose?"

"Canon Doughty it was," Cartright replied. "He's a perfect marvel, is that little man. He'd lead Trotzky by the hand as a little child if he wanted to, and wangle a subscription to Troop Funds out of a Soviet Commissar. But, come on, it's time for flag-down, then supper—you'll stay, I hope—and afterwards we'll regale you with a concert more hearty in effect than finished in performance."

The two climbed the slope to the brow of the little plateau, and there Heslet suddenly put his hand on his companion's arm to check him.

"I say, that's jolly, isn't it? Might be a lumber-camp on the Saskatoon."

They stood in silence for a moment and watched the group of boys round the fire—some of them in clear-cut silhouette and others bright-coloured in its ruddy glow.

Beyond in the Patrol camps lights were burning in the huts, and they could make out more boys engaged in the absorbing occupations of getting their blankets properly disposed for the night.

But it was the camp-fire which formed the most fascinating part of the picture. Here there was apparently much interest in the imminent boiling of a large saucepan, with a running accompaniment of laughter and boyish wit—above all, perhaps, a sense of complete happiness, as of a family reunited after the day's toil.

From the camp of the Fox Patrol came the lilt of a penny whistle, and from where the Peewits had their dwelling that ever-present camp sound of axe biting wood.

If the plateau was bright with flickering firelight, so were the surrounding trees dark and full of mystery; and it needed little stretch of the imagination to make of them a mighty forest haunted by bears and wolves and the stately moose, and peopled by Redskins with tomahawks and scalplocks.

Cartright turned to the other.

"What wouldn't I give for the skill to transfer that to canvas!" he said quietly. "For there before you is the game of Scouting in all its delightful simplicity. Don't you see the genius of the thing, Heslet? The return to the primeval instinct for all these things—the freedom and comradeship of natural surroundings, the call of the backwoods. Can you realise what it means to those youngsters to be transported here from their unutterable slums straight into the world of Fennimore Cooper and *The Last of the Mohicans*?

"There are many sides to Scouting—badge-winning, signalling, tests, the jolly kit—but the essence of the whole thing is this camping. Here we can get so easily and naturally at the spirit of it all, the one thing that really matters—the Law and Promise. Oh, it's a great game!"

"I'm beginning to think that it is," Heslet replied, smiling at the other's enthusiasm.

The chatter round the blazing logs died down, and presently there rose on the still air a voice clear and pure as a silver bell. It mounted and hung and quivered, as it were, about the very tree-tops, and then sank as swiftly down, to cease amidst a round of applause and cries of "Good for you, Monkey!"

"That's Monkey Owen," Cartright explained, in answer to the other's look of surprised inquiry. "Delightful, wasn't it? The boy has got a real gift, and we make the most of it. He's our star turn. Quaint little fellow—Welshman, of course, but born and bred in a dockland slum. You know, it's a marvel to me, Heslet, how the best in human character can find a footing under those appalling conditions. That boy's father is doing time at this moment for assaulting his mother, and she, I believe, is in hospital as a result. Monkey was left to fend for himself until Shawe, the Mission Warden, took him on as house-boy, and had him trained as solo chorister at one of the city churches. Now he is something of a celebrity in his small way—earns a bit of money at it, which all goes to his mother. A quiet, twisted fragment of humanity is our Monkey;

but he is liked by everyone because he interprets the law of the Good Turn very literally.

" You see that big fellow poking the fire? That's Reggie Hunt, also of the St. Jude's lot. He saved Monkey's life the first time they came down, and that is really what gave me the idea of the swimming-pool. Before we built it the boys used to go to an old quarry about a mile away—nasty dangerous place with a shallow ledge and then a sudden dip into fifteen feet of water.

" We had only been started six months at the time, and I was wrong to let them go there at all. Monkey couldn't swim then, and young Hunt could only struggle about a bit; but he went in with all his clothes on and fished him out. And now they are inseparable.

" But it gave me a shock, I can tell you, and so we set to work and built that pool, which is only four feet six in the deepest part, and absolutely safe. But now we really must have flag-down."

6

Heslet stood watching the little ceremony of lowering the flag, and then listened with interest to the list of camp duties which Cartright assigned to his Patrol Leaders for the following day.

Flag-down over, the Patrols were dismissed, and the whole troop gathered round the camp-fire for a supper of bread and cheese, biscuits and cocoa.

" Now then, Peewits, get busy with the washing-up," ordered Cartwright when the meal was over. " Otters, you are Cook Patrol; don't forget that we shall want another brew later on. The rest of you set to work and enlarge the circle round the fire—we'll stay out here to-night—and then go and get your blankets."

While he was speaking Canon Doughty came up the hill and joined the merry crowd. He had a word of chaff for the boys, and then appropriated a log seat between the other two men, with a grin at Heslet as he did so.

"Not had enough of camp yet? I somehow thought that I should find you still here."

"Very much here, *padre*," the other rejoined. "You couldn't shift me with a charge of dynamite until the sing-song is over. And I fancy," he added, "that I shall return to-morrow, if I may, to continue my initiation."

The Vicar looked quite happy at this.

"I don't think that there will be any marked objection—eh, Hugh? But it depends to a certain extent upon how you behave to-night. You must know, Mr. Heslet, that every visitor privileged to witness the solemn rite of the camp-fire sing-song is expected to contribute in kind—song, anecdote, or dance; we don't mind what—but contribute he must. Look at me, for instance, a Canon of the Church of England, Vicar of this ancient and important parish; even I have to bow to the unwritten law. They wouldn't let me inside the camp at night without my ancient banjo."

He produced the instrument in question from a tattered case, and Heslet laughed.

"I was given to understand something of the kind," he replied. "But I absolutely refuse to sing. I cannot sing; to dance I am ashamed; but I'll try my hand at a yarn if you like."

"We do not merely like—we command," said Cartright.

"Righto! But I told those young rascals of yours that they would have to charm the muse in me first."

"Don't know about charming your muse—more likely they'll startle it. But this conversation must now cease, and I'll summon the braves."

While the three had been talking the washing-up had been completed, the kettle left to boil, and the boys had disappeared to their separate camps.

The Scoutmaster piled more wood on the fire, waited until the whole plateau was bathed in its glow, and then, putting his hands to his mouth, sent out the thrice-repeated " too-whoo ! " of an owl.

Presently there came in answer from the three Patrol camps the sharp bark of a fox, the " ho-ick " of an otter, and the plaintive call of a peewit ; and three little processions in single file wound their way in solemn silence between the trees and up to the fire.

Each Scout wore his blanket cloakwise and had his scarf bound round his head. Silently they surrounded the fire, its flickering beams revealing faces not quite so solemn as the rest of their deportment. Still in silence the three leaders came forward and gravely presented blankets to the three men, that which they put round Cartright's shoulders being of vast dimensions and scarlet hue.

When the circle was complete the latter stretched out his hand majestically towards the glowing logs, and announced in a voice of becoming dignity : " Brother Scouts, the Council Fire is now open. To-night we welcome to our midst a traveller from afar, Mr. Heslet. He has been informed of the law of the Troop, which necessitates a contribution to our night's entertainment, and he has signified his acceptance. Let us, then, greet him with the combined Troop yell."

He raised his hand again, and, when he let it fall, the quiet of the night was rent by a staccato chant, " Evergreen, St. Jude's, Evergreen, St. Jude's, Evergree . . . n, wou . . . ou ! "—simple, but quite effective.

Heslet felt called upon to reply to this vociferous welcome.

" Scouts of Evergreen and St. Jude's," he said, " I feel deeply honoured by your reception of me—a wanderer, as your Scoutmaster said, from far lands. I can't play an instrument of music, I won't dance, and I haven't a voice like Monkey " (laughter and applause), " but when my turn comes I will tell you some of my experiences as a wanderer in many strange and distant countries."

More applause, and Heslet reseated himself on his log.

The next item was the song of the Evergreen Scouts, in the course of which was set forth much of their history : the building of the dam, the treks, the Cubs and Rovers, with a good sprinkling of topical allusions added as extra verses by the Scoutmaster, and greeted with much merriment by the chorus. The Vicar was then called upon, and taking up his banjo, he gave after a few preliminary chords a delightful rendering of two little plantation songs, both with good choruses and evidently great favourites with the boys.

" Now then, Monkey," said Ginger, " what abaht it ? " and " Come on, Monkey ; let's have ' Hiawatha ' " said the others ; and once more Heslet listened with delight to that wonderful voice, while the Scouts forbore to fidget and drank in every note ; and even the fire was allowed to collapse gently into a ruddy glow, which lit up the circle of eager faces, with their coloured scarves, in a way which made, to Heslet's mind, an apt setting for Monkey's effort, and would probably induce a quiet attention for his own, which he fancied would be the next demand. Nor was he wrong.

" What about your muse now, Heslet ? " queried the Vicar, when the last sweet notes had died away. " That should have charmed it if anything could."

" My muse is in fine fettle," the other replied. " I am not going to tell you a yarn exactly, but I hope all the same that what I say will interest you. You fellows, in a small way, have harnessed a part of Nature to your needs in that really wonderful little dam of yours, and in your shower-bath—even, I might say, in your camp-ovens, where you have so designed the flues that fire, one of the giants of Nature, places its heat exactly where you want it to be.

" So I am going to tell you something of the Nature-taming methods which have been used by man from the earliest times ; and show you that, in spite of modern machinery, the idea of many of these things remains with us now as it was then."

And he went on to tell them of the shadoof, the sakkieh, and the wheel of Archimedes, and of all sorts of simple but effective methods of water-raising and irrigation, and so, by gradual steps, up to the building of great barrage and canal schemes for utilising every drop of water—the most precious of all Nature's gifts in the East.

Heslet had a real knowledge of his subject, and handled it with the sure touch of one who has loved his work, and with the vivid imagination which had made that work so fruitful.

The fire sank lower and lower, and no one stirred to replenish it, for the boys had never heard anything quite like this before. It was, perhaps, a bold experiment, but, as he told it that night, it seemed that even the youngest of them read in his recital something of the colour of the Eastern world, its age-old romance, its ceaseless struggle against odds never dreamed of in their own lives.

" And now, Scouts, I've gone on long enough," he concluded. " But what I have been telling you was brought to my mind by your own efforts here in Evergreen. You fellows worked hard at that dam ; you made a success of it ; and now you are enjoying the result.

" One day you will be going out on your own, and the job which you have to do may seem a drudgery, a long lane without a turning. If that should happen, just think of your little dam here on the Sedge—and stick it out."

After he had finished speaking, and his audience, coming out of their trance, had expressed their appreciation in a way which boys have, Cartright announced that the Council Fire was now closed. They all stood with bared heads to sing two verses of " Abide with Me," the Scoutmaster said prayers, and then he packed them off to bed.

The three men went from hut to hut saying " Good-night," and afterwards started off down the slope, for it was getting late.

They reached the little coppice in silence, and then Cartright turned to Heslet and said : " I've never seen anyone grip those boys as you did—eh, Vicar ? "

" Agreed," the Vicar replied. " You scored a success first time out, Heslet—and it's not an easy thing to do with boys. I confess I can't hold 'em like that."

" Nice of you to say so," Heslet answered. " But they were a top-hole audience, and a good audience makes one talk."

" H'm," broke in Cartright, " I should be inclined to put it the other way about, and to say that a real good talk like yours makes its own audience. Bit of both, really, I suppose—kind of charmed circle. And yet I have it in my heart to pity you," he went on, with a shake of the head. " Your reputation may indeed be made, but your peace of mind is for ever shattered. You see, Heslet, you have ousted Monkey from his place as star turn. I dare say he'll be glad of a rest, but the young beggars will work you to death."

" For Heaven's sake, Hugh ! " exclaimed the Vicar in mock dismay, " wait till the float's well under, man, or you'll strike too soon."

Heslet laughed heartily. " Think that you've hooked me between you—eh, *padre* ? But you don't know this fish. He's a slippery beggar, and needs a light hand on the butt. But I admit," he added, " that your little red and green float is beginning to bob about a bit. If I were you I should pull the thing out and put on some fresh bait."

Cartright laughed. " Never fear ; we'll do that right enough. There are some most attractive grubs and worms left in the tin, and, if need be, we'll use 'em all. But I must be getting back to tuck my family up. Good-night ! " And with a handshake he turned on his heels and went back up the moonlit track.

7

When they reached the "Three Crows," and the Vicar had also taken his departure with a plea of early rising on the morrow, Heslet lit his pipe and went through into the garden.

The night was warm and still and moonlit, the air full of the scent of roses, and the old house, as he paused to look back upon it, stood out in all its mediæval quaintness and beauty.

Heslet chuckled softly to himself as he paced the length of the bowling-green and back, and his mind travelled swiftly over the events of the day, finding no cause for dissatisfaction therein.

He was something of a fatalist, a believer in Kismet; and, when he thought of all that had happened since his belated breakfast of coffee and eggs that morning, he could find it in his heart to thank the kindly fate which had introduced him in turn to Evergreen, Harry Giles, the *padre*, and Cartright, not to mention the "Three Crows" and its substantial proprietor.

It seemed to him that he had been following a series of steps cut before his feet by a careful friendly hand. For there had been no tangible reason why at breakfast that morning he should have selected this village out of all that were open to him within the limits of a day's ride, beyond the fact that the road over Sedgwick End had looked rather more inviting than any other on that hot and windless morning.

Then there had occurred the incident of the flat tyre. It might just as well have got him as far as the village inn; and there presumably he would have lunched, and then very likely passed on his way.

But the tyre had chosen to subside at the top of Sedgwick Bluff; and fate had sent him Harry; and Harry's certificate had formed an excuse for the Vicar's self-introduction, followed by his own visit to the Scout camp and his subsequent determination to stay awhile at the "Three Crows."

Heslet began to recall his conversation with the Vicar that afternoon, and he recognised with what knowledge and conviction the *padre* had spoken of the need and the opportunity, and to a stranger within his gates. Had there been any ulterior motive behind the singular eloquence and appeal of his words?

And then, again, he had seemed to warn him (Heslet) of the difficulty, almost the impossibility, of one who, like himself, had been a worker all his days and was still in the prime of life settling down to the uneventful peace of Evergreen. Certainly he had not said this in so many words, but was not that what he had meant? Had the *padre* summed him up with an instinct which is given to the few, but which he himself possessed? Was his discernment so quick and accurate that he had known at sight that here was a man who could never find all that he required for the rest of his days in Evergreen and rose-growing?

If so the Vicar was, as Cartright had said, something of a wonder. For Heslet knew that he was right.

There could be, he saw, too much of peace and useless ease of life in such a spot when there was work to be done, and the labourers were scarce out there in the desert places.

And then he began to picture to himself a Markham Heslet grafted on to the life of Evergreen—a restful picture, no doubt, but rather pathetic—of a man grown old before his time, dyspeptic and liverish through lack of excuse to keep brain and muscle active; a dear old dodderer with energy enough, perhaps, for the cultivation of his roses and such daily fussy little occupations as might be invented to stave off absolute boredom and help him to think of himself as of some real use in the world. But what would the world say? Talk of him—if they thought about it at all—as old Mark Heslet, quite a nice old boy with rather a jolly garden.

Even work with the boys, helping with the Scouts and Rovers, would be denied him here in Evergreen. For Heslet was a man who liked to run his own show, and they were already perfectly provided for in this little community; there was no need for a second string, though no doubt they would always be glad to see him.

But in any case that kind of position wouldn't suit him at all, because, for all his modesty, he recognised that he possessed a personality which, almost in spite of himself, dominated those with whom he came in contact.

No, it would not do. Whether or no the Vicar's words had been spoken with intent signified nothing. What *did* matter was that the man was indisputably right.

There *was* this work, this need for leadership; and he knew himself to have the leisure and the gift, proved in many an anxious moment away out there; and, moreover, even so short an experience as had been crowded into one afternoon and evening had convinced him that in this Scout idea lay all the machinery he was likely to require.

"A great game," Cartright had called it, and Heslet saw no reason to doubt him. Cartright and Doughty were both sensible men with no unnecessary trimmings and plenty of experience of its actual results. He had no doubt that Scouting was a great game as played by these boys and their leader.

The youngsters themselves could not, of course, see it as a game of life in miniature—the little ambitions, endeavours, successes, and sometimes failures; the spirit of comradeship; the sinking of self in the rights and requirements of others; the work of the good team; the cheerful acceptance of authority—in fact, the translation of their code from a hardly attained ideal into a living reality. Naturally they did not understand all that. But they loved it; and, loving it, could be guided and inspired in the playing—by the right man.

That, of course, Heslet had seen at once, was the whole

secret—the one thin line dividing success from failure. And it was just this which made him hesitate.

Was it, as the *padre* had hinted, a job where experience could compete on equal terms with youth? Extreme youth, perhaps, but fifty-eight was at the other end of the scale. It was true that he had been surprised that evening at his own feelings of bodily fitness and mental energy. But would they last, or were they the transient outcome of novel and stimulating surroundings, the glamour of a first impression under the best possible conditions?

It would be rather a different thing in a dockland slum. It would not be so easy there to simulate the romance and adventure of the backwoods, the setting which, according to Cartright, meant so much to the spirit of the game. He supposed that most games could be played almost anywhere after a fashion, but all the same the setting must make a difference. Here in Evergreen the ground was perfect; there in dockland a deal would have to be left to the imagination. Not that he was particularly worried on that score, for he knew that he possessed plenty of that commodity, and he realised also that others possibly less qualified than himself had overcome the difficulty. What they had done he would be safe in attempting; for Heslet had made up his mind—in one particular at any rate—that it was to dockland he would go if the next few days satisfied him of his capacity for giving these boys what they would require of him—sympathy, comradeship, and a firm hand over the stile.

As he walked slowly back to the inn he recalled the pathetic little incident of the *padre's* newspaper cutting, and he stopped for a moment to look at Blackett's roses spreading their fragrance on the night air. Satisfying thing, roses, Heslet thought, as he turned up the path to the house; but, after all, there were other things to claim the attention of one who could still do a man's work with the best of them. He had an idea at the back of his mind that a pack of boys away in a dark corner of London town would prove even more satisfying things to cultivate than roses, both to himself and to the country which claimed such service.

As he passed through the old oak door, Mr. Blackett greeted him with a capacious yawn.

" You be thinkin' of goin' to bed, sir, I do hope, for it be time I locked up."

Heslet looked at his watch, and saw to his surprise that it was past midnight.

" I'm sorry, Blackett," he replied. " No idea it was so late. That's what comes of thinking in a moonlit garden. It's a bad habit."

" Well, it be a good night for thinkin' ; and as for it bein' a bad habit—why that same depends on the thoughts, sir."

" You're a philosopher," laughed Heslet. " But I promise you that eleven-thirty will find me in bed as a rule. Which reminds me that I hope to stay here for a week or two. I hope that you have plenty of that cider."

" I'm glad to hear that you've made up your mind to stay, Mr. Heslet. You mind my words about them shorts ; and as for the cider, there's nigh sixty gallons of it yet. That should do, surely."

" I shall have to make it do," Heslet replied with assumed resignation, as he accepted a lighted candle and started to climb the narrow stairway. " First on the left at the top, isn't it ? Good-night."

8

For the whole of the following week the sun was unremitting in its attentions, and filled the little valley with a shimmering heat which distressed stout Mr. Blackett, but found Heslet in his natural element.

He spent part of the time in exploring the countryside, sometimes on his bicycle, but mostly on foot in company with the St. Jude's Scouts. School or work claimed their hosts of the Evergreen Troop, but during the evenings there was a reunion of the majority on the plateau, and on the Tuesday a general Troop meeting took place.

Heslet was particularly interested in this meeting, as it showed him the working of the Patrol System by which Cartright set so much store. It surprised him also to see the amount of responsibility which could be delegated to the older boys, and the thoroughness with which they instructed their Patrols in such things as campcraft, axemanship, and the many fascinating combinations of spars and rope. Nor was his own share negligible.

He had been diffident about offering his services until Cartright himself asked him to help.

" Johnnie keeps me pretty busy," he said, " and I can only get the evenings, Saturday afternoons and Sundays with the boys. It's St. Jude's I'm thinking about most. One or two of them work on farms during the day and earn a few shillings, but the rest have to look after themselves. Of course, Doughty and I come up here every now and again, and young Hunt is absolutely reliable. But it would be splendid if you could come up a bit, and, if you are really keen on learning something about the show, here is your chance."

" Just what I have been thinking," Heslet replied. " I should like to come and live in camp, if I may. As a matter of fact, I'm rather specially keen on trying my hand with the St. Jude's crowd, and should like to help to give them a good time. Most of them are out of work, I imagine, and not much to go back to ? "

" Slums and dirty streets, and dodging the cop, that's about all—and, of course, their own Troop. But Eakin's a busy man, and can't give much time to it; wonderful what he's done, considering the difficulties. If you really could do that, it would be first-rate."

This was on Monday, and on the following morning Heslet took up his quarters in a spare tent on the plateau.

Mr. Blackett witnessed his departure with a benevolent chuckle.

" Told you how it would be, sir, now didn't I ? " And Heslet agreed that so he had.

" You're a prophet as well as a philosopher, Blackett, but I'll keep on the room in case they are too much for me up there. And don't let all that cider go."

When Friday evening came he decided to go down to the Vicarage and talk things over with Canon Doughty.

The experiment of the last four days had been a success. He had, to use his own expression, " got in " with the boys.

There had been times, of course, when it had been necessary to assert a certain authority with the more turbulent members of his little gang, and on such occasions he had been delighted to find that a word was enough—just a quiet word and a straight look, which left no rancour, but which none the less impressed these youngsters of the slums that their new friend, for all his apparently easy-going nature, was one who meant what he said, and whose quiet word contained a hint of command—pleasant, perhaps, but quite inflexible.

Heslet had enjoyed himself more than he would have thought possible ; for not only was the acceptance of his authority, after one short, sharp passage, immediate, but he had been able to find much in his long experience of primitive places and peoples to aid him in interesting and instructing the boys.

He had, for instance, made something of a study of the methods of the native tracker, and was thus able to introduce an entirely new interest into their rambles about the country-side.

And, perhaps more than all, he had found the boys delightful companions, quick to catch hold of a new idea and with many original interpretations thereof which served to keep his own imagination stimulated, and acted as a spur to fresh efforts.

One whole morning had been given up to drum-signalling, using the Morse alphabet. The drums were only empty motor-oil tins provided by Joe Snippet, but they were quite effective with a thick belt of forest between the two stations, and it was voted to be a much more amusing way of learning signalling than by buzzer.

And now, after completing plans with Cartright for a great combined game on the following afternoon, Heslet went down to see Canon Doughty, and found him in a less cheerful mood than usual.

"Hullo, *padre*, what's up?" he inquired. "Just come from a funeral, or under the weather, or what?"

The Vicar smiled as he motioned Heslet to a seat. "Nobody ever dies in Evergreen," he replied, "and these heat waves agree with me, but this sort of thing doesn't," and he tossed a letter across to his companion. "Bit of a blow, that, eh? I was afraid it would come sooner or later. Eakin is the Scoutmaster of St. Jude's, as you know, Heslet. He's in the Eastern Telegraph Company, and, of course, he has to go where they send him. As he says, it's promotion, and he must take his chance; but it is rather hard on St. Jude's—third we've had in four years, and Eakin was far the best of the lot."

"Bad luck," said Heslet as he handed the letter back. "What will you do?"

"Well, it's hardly my job, though I hope it will be again some day. But I suppose Shawe will carry on somehow till he can get another man. The trouble is that Eakins don't grow on every tree."

"So I gather," said Heslet, and the conversation drifted on to other topics.

The game on Saturday afternoon was a great success, Cartright and Co. *versus* Heslet and his braves, with the Vicar in the difficult and onerous post of umpire.

And then there had been a final camp-fire concert in honour of the St. Jude's boys, who were due to return to their slums on Monday morning.

They were to be succeeded on the following Saturday by six more of their Troop, and it was probable that many of the present lot would return later in the year. So there was little of the undercurrent of sadness which so often haunts these occasions.

They all gave of their best, the *padre* particularly excelling himself, and when it came to Monkey's turn Heslet wandered away from the circle to the edge of the plateau, sat down with his back against a sentinel fir, and looked back on the scene which had so impressed his mind on that first evening.

The circle of coloured scarves and sombre-hued blankets, the ruddy glow illuminating one-half while it left the other in blackest silhouette, the happy, healthy faces of the boys, the warm-scented night all round—and Monkey's voice raised in that most plaintive of all airs, " Will ye no come back again ? "

There was something very appealing to Heslet in that clear young voice and in the answering chorus softly sung by the rest, " Better loved ye canna be ; will ye no come back again ? "

The genius of the whole thing ! The delightful simplicity of this Scouting game, which the boys loved ; and the essence of it all, a camp scene such as that which lay before him !

Of course they loved it ; how could they help themselves ? For in such a camp as this was enshrined all that is fullest of romance and chivalry and glorious adventure to a youngster ; and it is from the things and people we love that we learn most.

And so Heslet made his decision. He caused some little surprise to appear on the faces of his particular gang when he said on bidding them " Good-night," " I rather think, young men, that you and I will meet again."

On Sunday evening he packed his bag and called the innkeeper to him.

"I'm going up to town, Blackett," he explained. "I expect to be away three or four days, and I want this room kept for me."

When he returned on the following Friday evening there was much that he had to say to Canon Doughty, and he therefore lost no time in looking him up, finding him considerably more cheerful than on the occasion of his last visit.

"Hullo, *padre* ! wedding this time ? "

"Wrong again," said the other, as they settled themselves to talk. "Something even more cheering than that. I had a letter from Shawe this morning. Apparently he's got just the man we want."

"Quick work ! " commented Heslet, with the suspicion of a twinkle in his eyes.

"Yes, and that is just what makes me a bit doubtful about it. Shawe is a dear good fellow, but in the past some of his swans have turned out to be veritable little ganders. I hope that this isn't another case."

"I hope so indeed," murmured Heslet, as the twinkle deepened.

"Of course, as I said last time we met in this room, it's not really my business at all," the Vicar continued, "but somehow St. Jude's comes first with me. It's all wrong, I know, but I can't help it. Shawe doesn't even tell me his name—just says that he seems to be the right sort of man ; offers to live at the Mission and take entire charge of the boys. Sounds all right, doesn't it ? But I wish that I could trust Shawe's judgment. We have to be very careful about the men we get, and I like to know all about them first."

"Naturally," said Heslet, "I understand that. But do you remember the conversation we had the first day I met you, down in Blackett's garden ? "

The Vicar nodded.

"I've wondered since why you tackled a stranger

like that, and I flattered myself that it was because you saw then that we two had much in common. You may remember that you apologised at the end for boring me, *padre* ; but I think that you knew perfectly well at the time that I wasn't bored. I told you that you had started an idea in my mind—at that time I was rather on the look-out for ideas."

The other nodded again, and leant forward eagerly.

" You mean ? "

" I mean—well, to cut a long story short, that I have decided to go back to the desert. Don't look so alarmed, man ; you haven't succeeded in frightening me back to the East ; and, if I remember rightly, you said that you had a pet desert, too. Well, it happens to be yours which I have decided to occupy in future."

The Vicar whistled softly.

" So that's it, is it ? "

" Yes, that's just about it," Heslet went on. " Whether you intended to or not, *padre*, you laid the foundations of a promising career for me that afternoon, and, like a wise parent, straightway packed me off to school to prepare for it.

" You showed me the need, the boys showed me the possibilities, and now Eakin has vacated a little hole into which I can creep. And I'll try to be one of Shawe's successful swans," he added with a laugh—" that is to say, if you'll pass me. I believe that the boys have."

He got up to go, and the two men stood facing one another for a moment.

" Do you know, Heslet," the Vicar said, " this is the one thing of all others I could have wished ? I think I shall have a little brass plate fixed to the door of Blackett's summer-house with the inscription, " 'Even Bores have Their Uses.' "

" You do yourself an injustice, *padre*," Heslet replied, as he took up his hat and stick. " Write, rather, ' On this Spot Markham Heslet got another Chance.' Later on I hope that you may be able to add, ' And He took it.' "

V

A BROADCAST TALK TO SCOUTS

(*Delivered at Birmingham on February* 5, 1925)

GOOD-EVENING, Brother Scouts, wherever you may be. When first I was asked to broadcast a talk to you I was a bit puzzled to decide what I should say; because, although there are plenty of Scouting subjects one might talk about, it is rather difficult to think of something which nobody has said before. Probably I shall not succeed in doing so on this occasion, but at any rate I'll do my best.

The subject I have chosen is that of "The Scout Law and Camping."

"Why, that's two subjects!" I can almost hear some of you saying; or, "Now he's going to preach," others will exclaim; and yet others may think, "I know all about camping already."

And so you may switch the thing off, or whatever you do to a wireless receiver when you are fed up with it.

But wait just a minute; because, if you think any of these things, you are all wrong.

Firstly, the Scout Law and camping fit into each other like a hand into a glove; secondly, I've no intention of preaching anything but ordinary common sense; and thirdly, you don't know all about camping—very few people do. I, for one, certainly do not, and yet I have camped off and on most of my life, and in many different countries.

That's one of the joys of camping, to my mind. There is always something new to learn—some new gadget, a patent sort of tent, or a better way of turning a roach into a fried sole—if you can catch him first and cook him afterwards.

One never stops learning about camping, and my experience of a good many Scouts' camps is that some of you young fellows know precious little.

And yet, if we think about it, camping is, or should be, the most important part of a Scout's life.

By camping I don't mean just living in a tent instead of in a house, and grousing if the thing leaks.

I don't mean that any more than I consider that a boy is a Scout just because he happens to wear our uniform and has learnt the Scout Law off by heart. Anybody can do such things—a well-educated parrot could—but only a first-rate Scout can really camp well and at the same time bring the Scout Law into every part of his Scout life.

Now there are ten Scout Laws, aren't there ?—one for each finger and thumb you possess. So let us think of camp life as the glove and see how they fit in.

Number One says that a Scout's honour is to be trusted ; and in camp there are many occasions when you have to be trusted by your Scoutmaster to play the game.

He may have given you a job to do, or told you to watch the stew while he does something else ; or he expects you, because you wear the Scouts' uniform, to uphold the honour of the brotherhood wherever you may be, and not to do silly things which might make people in the village street turn, and watch, and wonder whether, after all, there *is* much good in Scouting.

So let us pass on to Number Two—a Scout is loyal. There is nothing more important in camp than loyalty.

There are so many things to be done if it is to be a success and run smoothly, and these things cannot be done unless everyone pulls his weight and a little bit extra. A Troop must be a good team in camp, and every member of the team must be loyal and play up hard the whole time.

Of course, Law Number Three tells us much the same thing: that of always watching out for extra things we can do to help the show along. But this Law also tells us our duty to others besides our own Scoutmaster and Troop.

For instance, there is the farmer who may have given you permission to camp. He is the fellow who is helping you to have a good time, and you owe him more than mere thanks.

I was talking to a farmer not so long ago, and he said: "I like having the Scouts down here; they brighten things up a bit. But I do wish they wouldn't leave my gates swinging, and would put things a bit tidier before they left. Anyhow, they're nought but boys, and I'll have 'em again if they care to come."

Well, I thought that was jolly good of him; and I found out afterwards that it had been that Troop's first camp. I expect that they'll do better next time. But it just shows, doesn't it? how careful you have to be.

A good camper isn't satisfied with merely remembering to shut gates and tidy up. He knows that his duty is to be useful, and that there may be ways in which he can repay the farmer who lets him use his land. So he keeps his eyes skinned to see how he can help.

Sometimes there are other Scout camps quite close to your own, and this will give you a chance to show that you are a brother to every other Scout.

Visit the other camps, and see if you cannot learn something new from them as well as getting to know some of your brother Scouts. And sometimes perhaps the village children will come out and watch all that is going on, and wish that they were Scouts too and could have a camp like yours. There may be something which you can do to give them a good time; and so we see Law Number Four fitting in nicely.

A Scout is a friend to all. I sometimes think, you know, that I like that Law almost best of the ten.

Friendship goes such a long way, and brings so much happiness, and spreads like the ripples in a pool. I like to think of you fellows when you go to camp showing friendship and kindness to all whom you may meet. You have such a good time yourselves that there is plenty to give away.

Think of those camp-fire concerts, for instance, and sometimes ask the people round to come and join in the fun. They appreciate it, and it is a friendly thing to do. It is also a courteous thing to do; but there are many ways of putting Number Five into practice in camp. You meet a lot of new people, especially when you go shopping in the village; and there are often quite a number of opportunities for doing those Good Turns, even down the length of a village street. A good Scout watches for such opportunities, and uses them when he finds them.

And so we reach Number Six. Not so easy to fit this one in, you may think.

But what about the poor old horse who may have to pull the dray all the way to camp with your tents and blankets and pots and pans all piled on the top? He wants a helping hand up some of the hills now and again. Some of you may say: "Oh, we always go to camp in a motor-lorry." Well, if so, you are lucky, and so is the horse.

But all the same I have seen many things in camp to illustrate this Law of Kindness to Animals. Sometimes boys catch fish, and put them in a bowl of water to slowly die. It may amuse the boys, but it doesn't amuse the fish. Once I remember that a Scout came back very proud of himself because he brought with him a waterhen's nest, all complete with eggs. He hadn't thought of the waterhen's feelings as she rushed about hunting for it afterwards, and I think he was rather surprised at the telling-off he got from his Scoutmaster.

Law Number Seven is the one about obedience, and this, of course, is an important part of team-work.

In any good game, whether it be Scouting or football, you have to be loyal to your side and do what the captain tells you.

Now in camp your Scoutmaster has a great deal to think about, and a lot of responsibility, and so it is only fair that most of the work should be done by his Patrol Leaders. Their job is to divide the work up equally amongst the Scouts in their Patrols. So a good camper always obeys his Patrol Leader, not only because this is the Seventh Scout Law, but also because he wants to make things easier for his Scoutmaster.

And he obeys quickly. There isn't much time for all that has to be done in camp in any case, and a slovenly job wastes what time there is.

And now for the one about keeping that cheery smile on your face. In all our camping we meet with difficulties, especially with our English climate. But, after all, they are part of the fun, and show of what stuff Scouts are made. Quite a lot of them can be avoided by learning as much as possible about camping before we go, and especially by seeing that canvas and cordage are in good condition.

But, all the same, annoying things sometimes happen. Somebody upsets the stew, or gets a headache, or slips on a rock and cuts his knee. But we smile and make fun of it, don't we ? especially if it doesn't happen to be our knee. Even the fellow with the headache is as cheerful as possible, because he knows that a glum face spoils camp for the others, and really doesn't make the headache any better.

Next comes Number Nine. It may be a little finger, but we've got to fit it in somewhere.

Of course, saving up helps to get a Scout to camp. I have even known of a Scout who saved up and helped to get another fello to camp who was too poor to do it all himself.

And even when we are in camp we can be thrifty and economical, especially about not wasting anything—food or wood, for instance. The best of it is, if we are careful about such things, we make the camp cheaper for everyone else.

And so I come at last to the Tenth Law—a Scout is clean in Thought, Word and Deed. I need, I think, say little about this Law, except that camp life—and, in fact, all life in the open air—should help you to that cleanliness of mind which is so necessary to health and happiness.

Well, we have worked through the Scout Law, and now, before they cut me off, I want to address a few words especially to Patrol Leaders.

I expect that quite a number of you who are listening to-night have reached that position of responsibility.

I wonder what sort you are ; because, as far as I can make out, there are two sorts of Patrol Leaders. One sort is the fellow whose only difference to the other Scouts in his Patrol lies in the fact that he wears two white stripes on his left breast-pocket ; the other sort is the fellow who really tries to lead his Patrol.

This takes some doing, I know, but it is the only sort which is worth while. Personally, I like to see Patrol Leaders who really do run their own little show, who determine to be the smartest in the Patrol, and always a little ahead of the others in the way of Scouting efficiency.

All very well, you may say, but how am I going to set about it? Of course, in many Troops (most Troops now, I hope) there are special nights set aside for training you Patrol Leaders, because your Scoutmaster realises that, if you are to lead properly, you ought to know just a bit more than the others, and so be able to teach them in your turn.

But even where this is not possible—and sometimes it is very difficult to arrange special instruction like this—still, you can do a great deal to help yourselves in the way of trying to improve your knowledge of Scouting, and keeping up things which you have once been taught but have since forgotten.

There is only one way of leading, and that is by personal example. If you are the right sort of Patrol Leader, what you do will be watched and followed by the other Scouts. If you are not the right sort, they may either follow you or ignore you altogether, and the Troop will suffer in consequence.

It is your job to see that, as far as you can, you make your Patrol the best in the Troop; and by best I don't mean the fellows who have the most badges, but the fellows who are really the best Scouts, remember their good turns, are proud of their uniform, turn up well at Troop meetings, and are always on the look-out for ways of helping the show along.

And in camp a good Patrol Leader has his best chance of showing what he is made of. As I said earlier on, you have got to be ready to take a lot of the work and worry off the shoulders of your Scoutmaster. You have your own little corner of the camp, so see that it is kept clean as a new pin. You are in charge of a tent at night; see that everyone has a decent chance to sleep and that the fresh air has a chance to get in. You may very likely have small boys in your Patrol who have never been to camp before; see that they are made comfortable and taught how to get the best out of their blankets. You should be especially careful of the young Scouts.

Sometimes they go to bed in damp clothes if there is no one to prevent them.

Sometimes the older fellows insist on talking when the younger ones want to go to sleep ; it is one of your jobs to watch out for this kind of thing and prevent it. Again, you should be the first to know if one of your Patrol feels unwell, and see that he tells the Scoutmaster.

And then there are all those things which have to be done in camp—digging rubbish-pits, bringing in wood and water and food supplies. Some of them are not much fun, but they have to be done, and it is the Patrol Leader who should be the first to help.

Camp is a great chance for you Leaders. See that you take it. Make yourselves really useful to your Scoutmaster ; try to take all the work off his hands ; see that the old Owls, or Ravens, or Bulls, or whatever may be the name of your Patrol, are real good campers, both in the way they do things and in the spirit with which they do them.

Remember that your Patrol is your own little show—your very own. If you never forget that, those two white stripes will mean something more than just the trouble of sewing them on.

Right at the beginning of this talk I told you that in my opinion camping is the most important part of a Scout's life. Well, I have tried to show you why I think so.

If anyone were to ask me whether So-and-So was a good Scout, I might reply : " Well, he looks quite a smart sort of fellow, doesn't he ? But I really cannot tell you whether he is a good Scout or not until I have been in camp with him for a day. That would show me at once."

In conclusion, I am glad to have had this opportunity of talking to you, Brother Scouts, because, you know, our Movement is often let down by bad camping.

One can understand it in a Troop of Tenderfeet, who really don't know any better, but there is not the same excuse for those who have done a lot of it.

Let us each and all resolve to make our camps the perfect piece of Scouting they should be, whether we are going to live in bell-tents for a fortnight or in little hike-tents for a week-end.

Let us try to recapture the spirit of the old pioneers—those gallant people who fared forth into an unknown country to found new homes for themselves and for those who came after them.

They had to face a trackless wilderness, hardship, hunger, thirst, and often savage enemies.

When we fare forth to our summer camps during the coming months we have none of those things before us, and the road is safe.

But at least we can take with us something of their team spirit, their unselfish work for the common good, their skill and readiness in overcoming difficulties, their cheerfulness, their love of Nature, and their simple faith in an all-wise God.

And let us, above all things, remember that the success and happiness of our camps depends upon each one of us doing his best, taking his share—and even more than his share—of the things which have to be done.

So good-night, good luck, and good camping to you all.

VI

THE DISCOVERY OF CUBMASTER WEBB

I

I HAD not been long settled in my little cottage on the outskirts of Sledborough when I was pounced upon, and then flattered and cajoled into doing a job of work.

It was quite useless for me to explain that I had not retired from the Indian Civil after thirty years hard labour for the purpose of seeking work at Sledborough, and that in point of fact I badly needed a rest; they simply would not have it, and they were really such dear people that it was hard to refuse them anything.

I should explain here that Sledborough considered itself very much alive and up to date—not at all like Penton and Adsleigh, both of which villages, it was reported, had peacefully slumbered through two Zeppelin raids, and had not even noticed the fiery descent of one of those monsters within half a mile of their respective boundaries. Nobody, of course, believed this, but it made a good story, and serves to show you exactly what the people of Penton and Adsleigh really were like.

Sledborough, on the other hand, had everything it could have—British Legion, Women's Institute, Scouts, Cubs, Guides, and Brownies; a Cricket Team, a Football Club (heroes of many a Junior League), a Choral Society, who went as far afield as South Wales in their search after cups and trophies; a Bowling Club; a Debating Society—in fact, every kind of institution that human ingenuity could devise. Very nice and quite as it should be, I suppose. But there is just one drawback to such an array of activities, and that is the impossibility of poor old people, broken like myself in the fight, getting any kind of a rest at all.

All these things, you see, want someone to run them. They require Secretaries, Scoutmasters, Treasurers, Captains, active patronage generally ; and, as I have said, it is very difficult to refuse to do one's share, especially after indulging in beautifully expressed panegyrics on " Duty " in the course of many a recruiting speech during the early days of the War. Nor is it possible to plead advancing age when the local incumbent, a man of immense and untiring energy, happens to be just twenty-two years one's senior.

Well, as I have said, they pounced upon me. They came both singly and in pairs, armed with bits of pasteboard, which were deposited in the tray kept for such things on the old oak dresser in my little hall. The pasteboards were a mere excuse ; the real business was the cajoling.

I regaled them with tea while I pleaded for that leisure to which I felt I was so justly entitled. I promised a modest subscription to this and a modest subscription to that, in the hope that I might buy them off ; but all to no purpose.

It appeared that I had arrived, for me, at the worst possible moment ; for them, just in the nick of time. Recently one or two people had tactlessly died and had left gaps hard to fill. Thus the Choral Society was lamentably weak in basses (I had been foolish enough to express a fondness for singing), and the Tennis Club had lost Major Brown, its enthusiastic Secretary. The Major, moreover, left no less than three aching voids, for he had also been District Commissioner of the Boy Scouts and Father of the British Legion.

I was informed, of course, that I was just the man for these diverse positions. With all my experience, etc., you who have been through this sort of thing know what wiles of speech necessity gives us all.

At last I fell, but it was only a partial capitulation. My fortress was taken, but I was allowed to march out with the honours of war. I made my own terms, and resolutely declined to tackle all three of the departed Major's activities, nor would I join the Choral Society; I really couldn't do it. Perhaps in time, but not all at once. I must find my level first and get to know people. Besides which I didn't play tennis—hadn't for years. It was useless to tell me that a Hon. Secretary needn't play. He couldn't be really interested unless he did, and I was not going to take up anything in which I could not feel a real interest.

The British Legion was rather different; so were the Scouts. Both were things of national importance, and it happened that I had seen something of the Boy Scouts in India. But even here I wanted to feel my way. I wasn't going to be rushed into all these things. I must learn something about them first. How does one learn about Boy Scouts? Books? Well, I would get all the books and read them. But experience is worth all the books ever written, and I would only accept on condition that I was allowed first to gain experience in my own way. Perhaps a closer acquaintance with Boy Scouts might show me as totally unfitted for the post; I might find that I disliked them intensely. It was no good telling me that everyone in Sledborough loved the Scouts; I wasn't born in Sledborough; I was beginning to wish that I had never heard of Sledborough. I must really be allowed to go about quietly for a bit and form my own judgment, and I would begin right at the beginning and tackle the Wolf Cubs first. If I could stand them the Scouts could follow. Meanwhile here was a guinea for their funds, and a guinea for the Legion, and another guinea for the Tennis Club.

And that was how I bought my footing in Sledborough, and incidentally came to know many delightful people, amongst whom I place Arthur Charles Webb first in chronological order.

Arthur Charles was the Cubmaster of the Sledborough Cubs—the 1st Sledborough Pack, to be exact—and if all that I was told about him was true (and I have no reason to doubt it) he must have been just the young man for the job. He was, in fact, very much the compleat Scout.

Quite early in my Sledborough days I had been informed that the 1st Sledborough Troop was actually the third Troop that was ever formed in the whole history of Scouting. How this was calculated I had been tactful enough to refrain from inquiring; but there it was—a glorious fact. And Arthur Charles was actually the first boy who had ever joined the 1st Sledborough Troop. So you will see that he was a very early edition indeed—almost, one might say, a first-folio Scout—and valuable accordingly; and, moreover, he had done everything he ought to have done—won a lot of badges, ended up as a King's Scout and Patrol Leader, and then become Cubmaster.

Our introduction came about at the garage where he was employed, and which belonged, I learnt afterwards, to his father.

I went down there for the purpose of inviting him to share my supper that evening.

"There are one or two matters which I want to talk over with you," I hinted mysteriously; "so, if you have nothing better to do, come round and see me; I want to ask your advice."

This last, I thought, was rather good. Everyone likes to be asked for his advice, though in all probability it is never taken when given. Anyhow, it did the trick, and produced Arthur Charles punctually on the stroke of eight.

"The fact is, Webb," I began when we were seated, "they have asked me to become District Commissioner of the Scouts here in the place of Major Brown. I haven't said 'Yes' and I haven't said 'No.' I said that I would take time to think about it; see if I liked the Scouts first, and that sort of thing. I've bought all the books, and I'm going to start at the beginning, which is, I believe, Wolf Cubs. Now I understand that you are O.C. Wolf Cubs, and that is why I asked you round for a chat."

Arthur Charles blushed and spilt his lemonade.

"Pleased to help you in any way I can, Major," he said. Every one calls me "Major"—I don't know why; I never was a major, but no matter. "Would you care to come round one evening and inspect my Cubs?"

I beamed at him. "That would be splendid—just what I want," I replied. "When does your Troop meet?" My education began at this point.

"We don't call them a Troop, Major, but a Pack—Troops of Scouts, but Packs of Cubs," I was politely informed.

"Ah!" said I, "I'm beginning to learn. I expect that you've forgotten more about Scouting than I shall ever get to know."

I don't somehow fancy that he quite understood this. He seemed to think that his leg was being pulled. I had meant to say something nice, but Arthur Charles looked as if I had said something rather rude. However, he issued an invitation for the following Friday evening at the hut in the Rectory grounds, and inquired whether I would care to have the *Wolf Cub Handbook*.

"I've got that, thanks," I told him, "and also one by Miss Barclay, and I've read 'em both. So long! See you Friday. Oh, and by the way, what ought I to wear? Footer shorts and a jersey?"

Webb smiled—was it a superior smile?—as he replied: "I should come as you are, Major. Good-night!" and thereupon departed.

Left to myself, I picked up the *Wolf Cub Handbook*, idly turned its pages, and thought about my visitor. A nice boy, I decided. Possibly a trifle pompous for his years and suffering a bit from swelled head; but, after all, he had been everything a Scout should be, and I was a mere beginner. No doubt he would be quite gentle with me at first, and willing to forgive early importunities. He was to be my mentor, my guide, my counsellor. I was to sit at his feet, and profit (I hoped) by his accumulated Scout-lore.

I had read all the books about Wolf Cubs without, be it said, fully grasping all their significance. I was now to see the real thing. Instead of pages and pictures I should be able to study thirty small boys and note the blossoming of their characters under the ministrations of a master gardener. It would be very exciting; but I felt that I must approach the matter in all due humility.

With this good resolution firmly fixed in my mind, I left my cottage at 6.15 on the following Friday evening.

As I drew near the Scout Hut in the Rectory grounds I became acutely aware of an indescribable pandemonium, a mixture of sounds of which the small boy alone has the secret. I peeped through a window, thinking that on the whole it would be more fair to young Webb if I were not to anticipate a formal introduction by an entry before the scheduled time.

The hut was a large ex-army affair, and, as far as the dust and the reflection from the window-pane would allow me to see, appeared to be full of small boys engaged in the process of mutual worrying on the floor, like so many litters of puppies. Two or three were running wildly round with bits of rope trying with small success to lassoo their squirming fellows, and emitting piercing screams of triumph or mortification the while.

It was an enlivening spectacle, and really made me feel quite young again. I felt, in fact, an almost irresistible impulse to take part in the romp. I hadn't had a good whole-hearted romp for years (you don't get them much in the Indian Civil), and I felt sure that it would do me good.

I have a theory that romping should be a compulsory part of everyone's daily existence. We all romp when we are young. Sometimes we rag when we get old enough to break up the mess furniture, but we are apt in after years to be rather ashamed of it in ourselves and to look upon it with disfavour in others. I really don't know why. There are so many people of our acquaintance to whom a daily romp—a real good mix-up on the floor—would spell salvation. . . . But I wander. . . . And here comes Cubmaster Webb in the full glory of creased shorts and tailored tunic.

The creaking of the Rectory gate gave me good warning of his approach, and I had time to assume a position of innocence as to the near presence of small boys before he came round the big clump of laurels.

"Good evening, Webb," I said. "I imagine from sundry sounds that this is where you meet. I got here a bit early, but thought I wouldn't go in till you came."

He seemed rather relieved at this.

"I am glad you waited, Major," he replied. "It would never do for you to see them until they are tidied up a bit. I'll go in and get them brushed down and let you know when we are formed up ready."

He opened the door, and immediately there was an amazing silence.

Good discipline, thought I; but I was conscious of a determination to add Arthur Charles to my list of people who should be compelled to romp once daily. I felt as if I should like to romp the crease out of his shorts, the perfect fit out of his tunic, even the parting out of his hair. But meanwhile I was to wait until everything was quite ready for a dignified reception.

The summons came in the form of a small, smart boy, who gave me a small, smart, heel-clicking salute, and asked me politely to step in. I did so, and found thirty cubs, with their uniforms nicely brushed, formed up in a circle with Webb in the centre. I was directed to step through the gap left by my guide, and the circle was then complete.

Absolute silence reigned, while sixty solemn eyes regarded me steadily. My reception was indeed one of great and becoming dignity ; and I thought with some amusement of young Webb's horror if he had arrived to find me buried under a pile of squirming youngsters on the floor.

The proceedings opened with the Wolf Cub Howl. I had read all about the Howl, but this was my first experience of the real thing. It was a small boy yell, it is true, but one to the production of which infinite thought must have been given. It was controlled, balanced, timed and regulated to the perfection of nicety—a really well-disciplined howl. But when it was all over, and an awkward pause indicated that I was expected to say something, I felt that a more boisterous and less well-controlled greeting would have been more natural, if perhaps less dignified.

However I said something nice, and inquired what was coming next.

" Oh, we'll show you some of the dances, Major," Webb replied. Then to the Cubs : " Dis . . . miss. Form up for Kaa."

The thirty small boys dismissed like a single guardsman, and decorously got into position for their dances.

I liked these ; there was more spontaneity about them, especially when they all tumbled about on the floor and imitated monkeys, at which accomplishment they were really very good. I turned to Arthur Charles.

" Capital ! " said I. " I've seen something of monkeys in India. . . . Who taught them that ? "

" That ? Oh, they do it naturally—like it best of all. Makes their kit in rather a mess, though," he replied. I was tempted to ask whether that really mattered, but a fresh dance was being undertaken, so I let it go.

Next came blindfold knot-tying, very accurately

performed ; then some physical jerks, wonderful in their precision ; and after this the proceedings terminated with another Howl and a final " Dis . . . miss " ; and the Cubs, with a polite " Good-night," departed.

Thus ended my first experience of Wolf Cubs, and I must own to a feeling of disappointment. I had to say nice things to young Webb. They were expected of one who had been privileged to inspect a crack Wolf Cub Pack. I summoned up all my enthusiasm, therefore, for their wonderful drilling, smart turn-out, and orderly behaviour, but I felt that something was lacking. I must go home and read the books again, because I was convinced that either my own or young Webb's interpretation of the spirit of the thing was somehow at fault.

2

The more I considered the matter during the next few days, the more unnatural the performance of these small boys appeared to me.

I argued in this wise : The natural small boy was the type I had seen and heard before Webb arrived—romping, noise and energy—and, as far as I could judge by the books and my own very limited experience of such matters, it was just this energy which should be a Cubmaster's greatest asset. A touch of discipline here and there, perhaps, firm and friendly, but not the barrack-square accuracy shown by the 1st Sledborough Pack. It wasn't natural. It seemed to me to be tampering too much with nature—small boy nature . . . as I should judge, a very delicate plant to rear.

Of course, I realised that I was a mere beginner, and that I should have to go about things very carefully if I wished to bring about any improvement. Webb had worked hard, and he was undoubtedly keen. His Pack was supposed to be the best in the county—at least, so I was told—and was considered a certain winner in the coming competition for the Challenge Totem Pole; and this, mark you, for the third year in succession.

Curiously enough, it was this same competition which proved the correctness of my theories, and incidentally the salvation of Arthur Charles Webb as a Cubmaster.

Only three weeks before the month in which the competition had to take place, Sledborough was visited by an epidemic of measles and it was considered a great misfortune when the edict went forth that the schools were to be closed, and the scratching of the favourites became necessary.

I regret to say that I personally heard of it with a feeling of relief. It would do no harm for some other Pack to carry off the trophy for a change. But this feeling was not shared by Webb. It was hardly reasonable to expect that it would be.

"Rather hard luck, you know, Major, after all our work. The boys had set their hearts on winning it, and now comes this rotten epidemic. Wharton will win it now, I suppose, and they aren't a patch on mine."

I took him to task on this point.

"Don't you think," I said, "that you have got this Totem Pole affair a bit out of proportion? Of course, it *is* hard on you having to scratch at the last moment; but the work you have put in isn't wasted. Winning isn't everything, Webb; it isn't even important. I will even go so far as to say that it is bad for your Pack to win too often. Personally, the only rotten thing I see in your having to scratch is the probability that the little beggars will go about boasting that they would have won it if they had been able to compete. I should have liked to have seen them squarely beaten by a better Pack."

Webb looked both surprised and hurt at this.

"But there isn't a better Pack," he remonstrated. "Why, at our last prize-giving the County Commissioner said——"

"My dear boy," I interrupted, rather testily I'm afraid, "with all due respect, I don't care what the

County Commissioner said. Mind you, I know very little about Wolf Cubs and Scouts, but I do know something of human nature. I've only seen one Pack in my life, and that is yours. Your Cubs are very smart and have lots of badges, but I reserve judgment as to whether or no they are the best Pack until I've seen the others. And, by the way, they want you to help judge the competition with me. Can you manage it? There are seven Packs entered, and we shall have to run round in my car and see them in their own clubrooms. We ought to manage two a night."

"I don't know whether I can," he started sulkily. Perhaps I had said a bit too much, but his self-sufficiency was beginning to try my patience.

"Now, look here, Webb, don't talk nonsense; you know you can," I broke in. "You agreed to teach me all you could about Cubs, and this competition is part of my education. If you won't do it, I shall begin to think that you would rather not see any Pack other than your own. Hardly in keeping with your fourth Scout Law, is it? And besides, your own boys can't meet while this epidemic is on. Your evenings are free. Have you ever visited another Pack since you became a Cubmaster?"

Arthur Charles was fain to confess that he had not.

"Very well, then," I continued, "it will be an education for you as well as for me. It will be so nice for you to see how much better the 1st Sledborough is than all the others—almost make up for not winning the Totem Pole, won't it?"

The touch of sulkiness left Webb's face, and he smiled; and when he smiled I liked the boy, and felt that there were possibilities in him.

"All right, Major, I'll come," he said. "Have you fixed any dates yet?"

"I have," I replied. "Alders End and Wharton next Tuesday evening—Alders End at 6.30 and Wharton at 7.30. Maybrick will give us supper afterwards."

And so it was arranged, and the first part of my little plot began to take shape.

I should state here that the idea of asking Webb to take part in the judging was not wholly mine, but the result of a conversation which I had had with Maybrick a week before.

Maybrick was curate of Wharton Priory and Cub-master of the Pack there. He was a distinct character—very short, very fat, very jolly, and full of the milk of human kindness. I had met him first at a meeting of the Local Association which I had been invited to attend in my capacity of prospective District Commissioner, presumably with the idea of bringing me up to the requisite pitch of enthusiasm for the cause.

I liked Maybrick at sight, and had walked part of the way home with him after the meeting. He was rather surprised (and I think considerably amused) when I told him that I was by way of being under instruction with Webb, and he wasted no time in summing that young man up.

" Keen boy, nice boy, very smart Pack and all that, but he just misses the mark and doesn't know it, or, if he did, wouldn't know why. I've known him all his life. Well brought up to a certain point; but old Nangarrow, his late Scoutmaster, made too much of a favourite of him; turned him into rather a self-conscious young prig, or did his best to. Thinks more of the outward and visible than of what really matters. Natural, I suppose, at his age . . ." a description which entirely agreed with my own conclusions.

This conversation was continued two days later when, at his request, I looked him up at his cottage near Wharton Priory.

I related my experience with Webb's Cubs—a recital which brought forth many a chuckle from Maybrick; and we thereupon hatched the plot.

Two things appeared to be essential if the salvation of Webb as a Cubmaster was to be accomplished. In the first place, he must be persuaded by his own observation that discipline can be maintained without barrack-square methods ; and secondly, he must learn the art of whole-hearted romping.

" My word ! " said the little curate, " what a shock he'd get if he saw the Reverend Thomas Maybrick, fat and elderly, dressed up as an Indian chief or a cannibal king ! He's got to see the thing, though, and realise that I can twist my small people round my little finger, in spite of the fact that I haven't a notion of drill and am totally unable to say " Dis . . . miss ! " like a Guards' sergeant-major. What about getting him to help you judge the competition now that his own show is knocked out ? "

I agreed that this might be the beginning of better things, and promised to sound him.

" Mind you, Major," Maybrick said at parting, " that boy's all right. He's got sound stuff in him and plenty of humour. I blame Nangarrow as much as anybody. What we've got to do is to remove a few layers of self-conceit and ruffle his hair a bit. I like the idea of his taking you under his wing for instructional purposes. Seems to me the boot is on the other leg, eh ? "

" Don't know much about that," I replied. " Between the two of you I ought to learn something about the genus Wolf Cub. After all, the best way of picking up the right line in a thing of this sort is to see two opposed methods and fix the happy mean. Instruction can be gained by seeing wrong methods as well as right. So he'll be some help, though possibly he would be hurt if he realised the part in my scheme of self-education which has been assigned to him."

" Possibly," chuckled Maybrick ; " anyhow, we've got to get him to the point where he can pass a shop window without studying his own reflection, and then laugh at himself for wanting to."

I smiled back at the little man. Here was an ally of parts.

"Maybrick," I said as we shook hands, "it's a whole-hearted, deep-laid conspiracy against a harmless, innocent, worthy young man. It is really too bad, and can only be excused if it ends in his improvement. Anyhow, I rely upon your co-operation next Tuesday evening. Show us Cubbing *à la* Maybrick at its best."

He thumped the region of his heart. "Major," said he, with mock dignity and a twinkle in his little round eyes, "you may rely upon the support of the Wolf Cubs of Wharton Priory. We would rather die than let you down. We feel that the honour of the Cub Brotherhood rests in our hands—don't we, Tommy?" (this last to a small boy who had just arrived with a message).

"Yes-sir," quoth Tommy, without in the least knowing what it was all about.

"Anyhow," Maybrick added, "I am inclined to doubt whether even Tommy and his brother-Cubs will recognise their Old Wolf come Tuesday."

As I drove my car home that evening I found myself speculating upon the possible result of our experiment.

The difficulty was that I had never seen Maybrick at work with his Pack, and there was just the possibility that his methods, compared with Webb's, might go too far in the opposite direction. But on the whole I felt that it was safe to take a chance here. The little curate was very human, and had to my mind just that touch of sympathetic understanding, combined with a very attractive personality, which would enable him to get at the heart of Scouting or Cubbing. I could quite understand his claim to be able to twist his small people round his little finger, and it was just this that I was so anxious for them to demonstrate to Arthur Charles.

He, poor fellow—the unconscious victim of our scheming—looked at the matter from a different angle, and I was convinced that it was the wrong angle. Whether our experiment would have the desired result only Tuesday night and time would show. But of one thing I was very certain, and that was that it would be far more salutary for him to see and ponder over the difference for himself, and thereafter perhaps remodel his methods without further suggestion from outside.

If such a state of mind could be induced in him, then I felt that our plotting would be justified.

3

It was raining hard on the following Tuesday when we set out at 6.15, and I had to put up the hood of the car ; also we had a puncture a mile out of Sledborough, which necessitated Webb getting out and helping me to ship the spare wheel. We both got very dirty doing this, but he did his share with a will, and appeared to have quite recovered from his fit of sulks. I fancy that he had been gently chaffed on more than one occasion by the Reverend Thomas, and was looking forward to an opportunity for official criticism of that gentleman's Pack.

We managed to get a wash at the little garage at Alders End, where I put up the car, and then walked down to the school where we were to judge our first lot. I need not say much about them. The competition was a simple one—a Pack evening to occupy not less than half nor more than three-quarters of an hour. The Alders End Cubs were new to the game, both the boys and their Cubmaster (the Schoolmaster's daughter) being palpably nervous, and Webb thought that it was a waste of time for them to have entered at all. I disagreed with this, and complimented them upon showing the proper spirit.

Then we went on to Wharton, and I must say that Maybrick's Cubs were lucky in their room. The old priory was a ruin, only one corner of it being at all habitable; and the owner, I learnt, lived in the hope of one day discovering some wealthy man who would buy up the place for the fun of rebuilding it. Meanwhile he had been cajoled by the popular little curate into allowing the Cubs to use the old hall as a playroom, and had even installed a stove to heat the place in winter.

It was an ideal room for the purpose, full of mysterious recesses, with old panelling, a magnificent beamed roof and a huge stone fire-place. Maybrick had utilised the roof-beams for simple gymnastic apparatus. As he said when he first showed me round, all boys will climb, and they might just as well learn the right way.

As Webb and I entered the short drive leading up to the old place we were met by one of the Cubs. He saluted and announced: "Please, sir, Mr. Maybrick said as I was to give you this, and would you open it before you come in;" and then he ran off and left me with a note in my hand to the effect that we must not be surprised to find the room empty on our arrival.

"It is intended as no disrespect to our honoured visitors," wrote Maybrick, "but is part of the show. When you enter please seat yourselves by the inglenook in the fire-place and patiently await events."

"Very mysterious," remarked Webb. "Wonder what they're up to?"

I led the way inside, and we seated ourselves according to instructions. "That no doubt we shall presently find out," I replied.

I was right. We did.

The room was a large one, and rather dark, owing to a certain amount of stained glass in the windows. I have already said that it was full of recesses. Some of these were curtained off, and one was got up to represent a rocky cave by means of rather cleverly painted canvas. In the centre of the floor there was a small platform camouflaged in the same manner.

Absolute silence reigned. Presently, however, a series of growls and grunts issued from the cave, and then there came forth from its cavernous depths a large shaggy form, into the make-up of which the domestic hearthrug had evidently been impressed. But it was wonderfully life-like all the same, even to the shaggy head, fierce eyes, great teeth and swishing tail. On leaving its den this strange beast shambled forward a few steps, lifted its head and very audibly sniffed the air.

" I am the Old Wolf," it growled fiercely. " Where are my Cubs ? Where is the Pack to which nightly at full moon I explain the mysteries of the jungle ? This is the appointed hour and there the Council Rock. Perchance they think that they are old enough to hunt for themselves, but I, the Old Wolf, know better. Not for many moons yet will they have mastered my secrets. I must summon them."

The creature then proceeded to climb cumbrously upon the Council Rock, lifted its head and emitted an awe-inspiring howl. " Ou . . . ooo ! Ou . . . ooo ! Ou . . . ooo ! " it wailed in long-drawn cadence, and ended by producing a series of sharp peremptory barks, into which was woven the word " Pack."

Immediately there was an answering chorus of shrill howls, and Cubs appeared from eveywhere as if by magic. Evidently the room had been full of them the whole time we had been sitting there. Some emerged from a pile of sacking in a corner, some crawled from the curtained recesses, two from the cave itself ; one crawled from under the Council Rock, one climbed in through an open window, and the rest appeared from the roof, swarming down the ropes suspended from its blackened beams.

For a minute pandemonium reigned supreme. They rolled upon each other, they squealed, turned somersaults, pick-a-backed, leap-frogged and gambolled like a lot of puppies. Suddenly, however, the Old Wolf raised one paw. " Silence, my children," he growled. " Such behaviour round the Council Rock is not seemly. Form the magic circle and listen to my wisdom."

There was instant quiet and obedience. The little fellows formed up in a circle round their Cubmaster and remained quite still. The paw was once more lifted, and the cavernous voice announced: "First, my children, you will greet the jungle-folk and renew your promise"; and thereupon the Pack squatted and gave the Wolf Cub Howl, rounding it off with a remarkably good imitation of the real thing.

"A big ragged," I heard Arthur Charles mutter, as he scribbled an entry in his notebook, "and that noise at the end isn't official." But I was too absorbed with the proceedings to take any notice of him at the moment.

When the last notes of the Howl had died away the Old Wolf took up the tale once more.

"I will tell you something of these jungle-folk, my children, that you may learn their ways and thus see what to copy and what to avoid." And then with delightful humour he told us of Bagheera the Wise, of Baloo the Pompous, of Kaa the Crafty, of the impudence and destructiveness of the Bandarlog—a little recital which was a gem of storytelling in itself, and which held the boys spellbound.

"Now," said he in conclusion, "lest you forget this lesson, you shall perform the ceremonial dances, so that you may see for yourselves how crafty is Kaa, how wise is Bagheera, how pompous is Baloo, and how tiresome and useless are the Bandarlog."

With that the boys formed up for the dance of Kaa, and for the first time I realised the significance of these simple dances and the fact that they portray many types of character to be met with in the everyday jungle of human society. Not that the boys did them particularly well; on the contrary, their performance was probably less accurate than that of the 1st Sledborough. But there was infinitely more life and fun in it, and they undoubtedly gained in effect from their very natural and delightful introduction.

I could see out of the corner of my eye that Webb was impressed. He had given up writing notes in his book and was concentrating his attention on the performance itself.

" I say, that's jolly good, you know ! " he exclaimed when it was over. " I never thought there was anything in those dances. I suppose he won't wear that skin all the evening, will he ? Must be rather hot."

We were not left long in doubt on this point. The Old Wolf was already engaged in untying a complicated arrangement of strings about his person. This done to his satisfaction, he calmly remarked : " The heat of summer is upon us. Now that the ceremonial dances are over it is time that I shed my heavy winter coat." With these words he allowed his strange garment to drop from him and appeared as a very stout, jolly and perspiring Cubmaster.

" My word ! that's better," he continued, mopping his brow. " Couldn't have stood that kit much longer. Now, Cubs, form the circle. You all know that this evening you are being judged for the competition by Major Caryll and Mr. Webb. We may win or we may lose. If we win we shall be glad. If we lose we shan't mind—eh ? "

Chorus : " No-sir."

" Anyhow, we are going to do our best—eh ? "

Chorus : " Yes-sir."

" That's all right then. Sixers, call the roll, and report to your Pack Leader."

While the Pack Leader—a bright, sturdy-looking youngster, full of importance—was transacting this part of the business, Maybrick strolled across to us and shook hands.

" Hope you didn't mind the mystery surrounding your welcome," he laughed. " I'm afraid we don't always keep to the book, so mind you tell us if there is anything wrong. We Cubmasters are always ready to learn, aren't we, Webb ? "

I never liked the boy so much as I did when he gave his answer :

"I'm beginning to think, Mr. Maybrick, that I didn't know anything about Cubs till I entered this room."

Maybrick gave him a quick, kindly look and laid a friendly hand on his shoulder.

"That's a very generous thing for you to say, Webb," he said. "But you do yourself an injustice. I believe that we can both learn things from the other, and I hope that we shall. But now I must carry on, or you'll go and penalise us for overtime and a late supper. We are going to show you ten minutes' work by the three Sixes in their own corners. Sixers, take charge!"

During the next ten minutes I had occasion to remark to Webb that the Sixers knew their job pretty well, and he agreed.

He wasn't quite so certain about the manner of the physical jerks which followed. He himself seemed to have a passion for physical jerks as jerks. Maybrick, on the other hand, interpreted the word "jerks" to include anything which caused a natural reflex of the muscles ; anyhow, the result was wholly delightful.

He produced first a small sack, from which he tumbled a lot of little bells threaded on strings. These the Cubs fastened round their legs under the fold-over of their stockings. Then he took a fiddle from the cupboard and struck up a lively tune.

The boys had been well taught, and their dancing was one of the prettiest and most spontaneous things I have ever seen.

"As a matter of fact," the little man confided to us while they were reforming for the second dance, "we are getting this up as a good turn for the Parish Fête, and we badly wanted an audience to practise on."

I have always thought that natural dancing by children is one of the jolliest things imaginable ; it expresses so fully the joy of being young. On the present occasion

I could have watched till midnight. However, there was the poor fiddler to consider, for the evening was warm and, as I have said before, he was far from thin.

After three or four changes he put away his fiddle, the bells were returned to the sack, and the Pack was summoned once more to the Council Rock.

" Now, my small Cubs," said Maybrick, " you have already had your yarn, and we want something to keep us all still and easy for a bit, so we will have the game of ' Worry.' " He turned to us. " I should explain that the great game of ' Worry ' consists of a bombardment of the poor Cubmaster with all sorts of questions by his Pack. The questions have to be sensible ones, and can cover every kind of knowledge which the Cubmaster can reasonably be expected to possess. After asking his question the Cub begins to count ten. If the Cubmaster cannot produce the answer before that period expires he loses a life ; and this is where the awful part of the game comes in. If he should be so unfortunate as to lose three lives during the eighteen questions, he has to surrender himself to the Pack to be dealt with as they think fit. If he doesn't lose more than two lives the Pack surrenders to him. Whatever the way of it, the result is inevitably some sort of a rough-and-tumble. Now, ready ? "

It was a most instructive and amusing game, and it became really exciting when two lives had been lost with only two questions to go. It was like being dormy two down in a golf match. In this case poor Maybrick was stumped on the last green—rather a mixing of metaphors—what I mean to say is that he failed miserably at the very last question, " How many miles long is the Dead Sea ? " He tried in vain to save himself by making a wild guess. Just as the young rascal who had asked it had reached eight in the count, he shot his bolt. " One hundred and twenty," he hazarded.

There was a chorus of triumph.

" No-sir ; fifty-five, sir."

" How on earth do you know, you young imps ? " he asked.

Chorus : " Please, sir, teacher said so in Sunday-school, sir."

Maybrick surrendered at this.

" All right," he said, " I'm out. What's my fate to be ? Nothing too hot, I hope. I'll go to the cave while you consider the matter."

He went off to his lair with a wink at us, and thereafter there was a great but subdued jabbering by the Pack in a far corner. They then solemnly reformed the circle and summoned him to their midst.

" Well, what awful fate is in store for me ? " he queried.

Up spake the Pack Leader : " The sentence of the Pack is that you are given till I count ten to climb up to the roof ; then you're the hunter up a tree and we are hungry wolves dying of starvation, and you've got to get down somehow and escape. If you reach the door you're all right, but if you don't you'll be torn to pieces and your blood will stain the snow an awful red. One, two, three . . ."

" My word ! " gasped the unhappy Maybrick, " what an awful death ! " and straightway swarmed with amazing rapidity up the nearest rope.

The Pack meanwhile danced about the floor snarling and snapping at the small, rotund figure straddled across one of the roof-beams.

The situation was certainly not without its thrill, for he had a choice of three ropes and a rope-ladder by which to make his descent. It was a terrible choice to have to make. He could get from one main beam to another across the tie-beams, and at first sight the best plan would appear to be to descend by the rope hanging nearest salvation. But Maybrick argued differently. The yapping horde below would naturally concentrate near the door, and he evidently considered his only chance of breaking through lay in a burst of speed from a sufficient distance to enable him to use his weight to the best advantage. He made, therefore, as if to use the rope by the door, which was hanging within two feet of the wall.

The fierce and rampant wolves below concentrated at this spot; but they did not anticipate the next move of their intended victim, and it nearly caught them napping. A second rope hung from a beam about fifteen feet distant. With one mighty kick of both feet Maybrick launched himself in a great swing, jumped nimbly from one rope to another in mid-air, and had reached the ground and started at a bound for the door before the boys, or ourselves for that matter, had recovered from wide-eyed astonishment.

It looked for the moment as if he would win to freedom; but only for a moment, for, with a wild howl, the Pack were on him. They clung to both his legs, they seized his arms, clambered on to his back, and the whole lot went down squirming on the floor.

They did give him a time, those youngsters, what with rolling on him, pummelling him, and sitting on his head. At last a muffled voice could be heard appealing for mercy. "All right, I'm dead, or shall be jolly soon if some of you young beggars don't get off me."

"He's dead," chanted the Pack; "he's dead and we've eaten him up—eaten him up."

Having assured themselves on this point, they joined hands and broke into an impromptu war-dance, while their dishevelled Cubmaster picked himself up from the floor and straightened himself out a bit.

"You just about have eaten me up, you young monkeys," he groaned as he searched the floor for a vanished brace-button. "My word! you wait till I win next time! Hullo! it's nearly 8.30. . . . Pack! Pack! Pack!"

The effect was immediate. Instantly there was silence. The uproar might have been cut off with a sharp knife as the boys fell in round the Council Rock.

"Well, Cubs," said Maybrick, "we've all had a very jolly evening—at least I'm sure that you have, and what's left of me has enjoyed it, too; so shall we just take our caps off, and for a few moments thank God for giving us this jolly evening, for health and youth to enjoy it, for the comfortable homes we are going back to, and for all His mercies to us? And don't let us forget our brother-Cubs all over the world. Let us pray that He will bless them too, and give them all the happiness He has given us. Let us pray that He will help us to keep the Law of the Wolf Cub Pack and our Promise. And let us never forget other people, and our Good Turns to them."

And then followed a short silence—a very impressive and reverent silence—and afterwards the Lord's Prayer and a simple blessing.

The sincere effectiveness of the whole scene spoke of the affection which these little fellows had for their Cubmaster, and his simple blessing seemed to me to hold all the deep love he had for each one of them, and to be indeed a perfect expression of the relations between Cubmaster and Pack.

Perhaps I learnt more in those few minutes of the power of true guidance and leadership and of the underlying possibilities of this delightful game than I had understood hitherto. I am certain that young Webb was affected in the same way. I glanced at him, and it seemed as if he, too, had fallen under the spell of Maybrick's personality.

Prayers over, the little man turned to me. "Major," said he, "you and Webb must come up here and take the last Howl as an expression of our happiness at having had you both with us. We hope—don't we, Cubs?—that you will pay us many more visits."

"Yes-sir," yelled the Pack in chorus, and then gave us the Grand Howl with a vigour which seemed to say that they really hadn't had a chance to use their lungs till that moment.

Lastly, the room was put tidy by the Orderly Six, the door was locked, and we all trooped out into the road.

The Cubs had still so much to say to their Cubmaster that Webb and I fell behind and brought up the rear of the procession.

"I say," said the boy, "do you see that, Major? The little beggars won't let him go. I've never imagined anything like that. They must love him, mustn't they?"

There could be little doubt on that score. They held on to each arm chattering and laughing and all trying to get an answer to a large variety of questions.

"They do," I replied. "A regular Pied Piper is Maybrick."

At length we reached the gate of his little cottage, the last cheery "Good-nights" were said, and the boys trooped off under an early moon to their several homes.

"Come along in, both," said our host. "I'm afraid that we are rather late; but it's all cold, bar the soup, and that will soon warm up again while we are having a wash, which I for one badly need."

During the meal conversation was mainly between Maybrick and myself. I discovered that he had been attached for three years to a C.M.S. Mission in Travancore; and so we talked a lot about India.

Webb was very silent, both then and during the drive home, and declined my invitation to come in for a final smoke.

"Not to-night, thanks, Major," he said; "I've got a lot to think about."

4

It was nearly a week before I saw him again. I was just thinking after dinner of strolling down to his house when he opened my gate and came up the little rose-bordered path.

"Good!" said I; "you've saved a lazy man a walk. I was just coming down to your place to fix up our next two visits, Penton and Adsleigh. Come along in and smoke your pipe."

The boy was not looking very well, I thought, as the lamplight showed me his face—rather tired and dis-spirited. I said as much, but he passed it off naturally enough.

"Rather a heavy day at the works, Major. Colonel Enson's car broke its back axle, and we only got the new one yesterday. Says he must have it first thing to-morrow. We got the job through all right, but it was hot work down in the pit."

I tendered my sympathy while I passed the matches and he lit up ; and then he suddenly looked at me through the haze of smoke.

"I say, Major, what toppers they are, aren't they ?"

"What, Daimlers ?" I replied. "Yes, jolly good cars. I used to have one when I first came home before the War, but can't run to it now. However, that little Wolseley of mine does me top-hole."

Webb laughed. "I wasn't thinking of motors, Major, but of Mr. Maybrick's Cubs. Mine aren't a patch on his."

This was a most surprising statement coming from Webb, and I hope that I showed no sign of having received a shock.

"My dear boy," I said, "nonsense ! Your Cubs are every bit as good as the Wharton crowd—that is to say, as far as material goes. They are delightful children, every one of them."

"Oh, I didn't mean quite that," he replied, "but the whole show, and especially the way they hung round him going home."

He looked at me a bit wistfully, and then turned away again. "I'd give anything if mine would do that."

I must here confess to a little, and rather shameless, glow of satisfaction at his words. But, at the same time, the boy was clearly troubled, and I felt very sorry for him, for I knew that he had gone through a bad time since that evening. His very keenness for his Pack only made it the more difficult, and I saw that, if I was to give him the help he deserved, I should have to be very careful to wound his feelings as little as possible.

"I'm very glad, Arthur, that you came round to me like this. It was jolly good of you, because I know that what you've just said was not at all an easy thing for you to say, especially perhaps to me. After all, I'm a beginner at the Scouting game, and you are a veteran of many years' service, but I believe that I can help you all the same.

"You see, Arthur, I have knocked about the world a good deal, and it has been part of my job in life to study my fellow-man. We older people can naturally size up a situation quicker than fellows of your age can; we shouldn't be much good at our jobs if we could not; and it may therefore be that, in spite of the short time I have been on this particular job, I am in a position to give you some sound advice. Mind, I don't press it on you. You have heard the old saying that half the world is made up of people who give advice and the other half of those who won't take it. So, if I *do* give it, I want you to feel yourself free to take it or not as you think fit.

"Now, the difference between Maybrick's Pack and yours is not in the boys; they have got nothing at all to do with it. It lies in the outlook of their respective Cubmasters—in fact, it is a difference in personality."

Here Webb looked up eagerly.

"If you won't think me silly for asking such a question, Major, what is personality? Of course, I know it more or less when I see it, but what exactly is it? I mean, is it a thing one is either born with or has to go without altogether, or what?"

"Well," I replied with a smile, "you've asked me a bit of a poser there. It's not an easy thing to define. As you say, one recognises it subconsciously, so to speak, when one sees it, but—well, I'll tell you my idea of what the term means. To start with, I'll try to answer the last part of your question. I believe we are all born with what I may call the power of personality in us, but whether it comes out or no in after years depends on many things—upbringing, for instance, home surroundings, heredity, or, perhaps more than anything, opportunity. If it comes out very early in life we call it 'character'; but the two things are not quite the same. Character may lead a person off at a tangent; personality —the right kind of personality—acts as a steadier. In a word, it is the gift of leadership. The two things are bound up one with the other, and they both come (though, mind you, this may not always be apparent) from an innate sympathy with, and love for, one's kind, or even for those who are not our fellow-creatures.

"Let me give you a few illustrations. We all know that some people have a wonderful gift of attraction for animals; dogs are instinctively attracted to those who love them, because they have the power of sensing this love in the human. The same thing with horses. Some people can do anything with almost any horse where others would be hopelessly at sea. And so to a much greater extent with their fellow-men. Just look at the War. There we had the most wonderful examples of sheer personality—the young boys who got a commission straight from school, who had never handled men before. How many instances, were there not? of wonderful leadership on their part!

"It was personality, Arthur; it was the simple fact that to many of them was given the power of sympathising with and loving their men. It is a power which overcomes all caste, so-called class distinction—a power which never insults by the condescension of the top-dog for those under him—just a natural feeling which made some of these boys aware that it was a privilege to be able to think of every man in their platoon or troop or section as a comrade.

"And their men responded. They sensed the sympathy in their officer ; and, though he might have been only half the age of many of them, they accepted him as their leader and would follow where he led.

"And it's the same with children. It's probably even stronger with them, because the very young have a disturbing power of sizing up their elders. They know at once whom they can trust and to whom they can freely give their love. Look at Maybrick the other evening—a fat, funny-looking little parson, always with a joke on his lips, but one of the sincerest little men I've ever met. His Cubs worship him ; anyone can see that. They know instinctively that he loves them, and that's all they want. He doesn't need to shout orders at them, or even be very strict ; and yet have you ever seen a better demonstration of instant obedience than when he said, 'Pack, Pack !' in the middle of their war-dance ? And you remember that they'd just been absorbed in the cheerful occupation of sitting on his head. Well, Arthur, that's what I call personality."

Webb nodded in comprehension.

"And now I'm getting to the point," I continued. "I firmly believe that you have exactly the same power in you."

The boy shook his head gloomily.

"Yes, I believe that you have," I went on. "How long have you been going now ? Eight months, isn't it ? And you told me that you have only lost one Cub in all that time. So the boys like you, that's certain ; and what's more, they and their parents trust you. Thank goodness there is no sloppy sentimentality about you, Webb ! Some people practise this and call it sympathetic understanding ; but it's unhealthy, and is probably one of the greatest dangers in a movement of this sort. There is nothing of that about you. Your fault lies rather in the opposite direction. All that drill—now I shall hurt your feelings, Arthur, but don't mind me and what I say—all that drill and wonderful meticulous accuracy, the physical jerks, even the perfection of the Howl, the subdued order of the whole show, these things are foreign to the very natures of small boys of nine. There is bound to come a time when they'll get bored—I think it's much to your credit that yours haven't already—and you'll get bored too.

"When I came to see them, before you arrived on the scene, I watched them through the window. They were playing a wonderful game of some sort, and getting themselves thoroughly happy and untidy. I wanted to join in the romp myself, but didn't because I thought it hardly fair on you. And then when you came in everything was put terribly tidy and in order, and the little fellows acted just as if you'd put 'em all in a bottle and crammed down the cork.

"Maybrick's method is different. There you have excitement, laughter, fun all the time, and then a most glorious small boys' game, just what they like. You see, Maybrick has studied them, and has the power of throwing back his forty odd years and becoming a boy of nine again. It is far easier to do this at forty than at twenty. At twenty self-consciousness gets in the way; at forty our perspective has deepened. Learn to play with your Cubs, Arthur.

"You said just now that you longed for them to crowd round you like his did round little Maybrick. They will if you give them the least encouragement. At present they are shy of you; they like you, but they're shy, simply because they look upon you more as the man who comes and drills them twice weekly than as a playmate always ready for a bit of fun. They'll come thronging to you fast enough if you'll let 'em sit on your head sometimes, but not if you merely stand them in a row and shout 'Alert!' or 'Dismiss!' at stated intervals. No need to alter things all at once; but gradually learn the art of playmate, and you'll find, Arthur, that your control over them is increased, not diminished. And you'll probably find this also: that they'll bring their little childish troubles to you as they do to Maybrick. There will be that subtle bond of sympathy which is so infinitely stronger than anything obtained by barrack-square methods. And now, look here! What a sermon I've given you! I've missed my vocation. I feel as if I ought to announce the next hymn. Let's split a bottle of cider instead."

With that I left the room in order to ransack my dining-room sideboard for bottle and glasses. When I came back the boy seemed to have quite shaken off his depression, and his eyes shone eagerly as he said: "I say, Major, do you really think I could do all that? You've bucked me up tremendously. But there is one thing I don't quite see. How on earth am I to start? If I suddenly begin barging about, they'll probably think that I've gone dotty."

"I don't think they will," I replied, smiling at his eagerness, "though I see your difficulty. Look here! what do you say to this? Why not let me take them for one or two meetings, and break them in, so to speak?"

He shook his head. "Thanks; it's jolly good of you, and I believe everything that you've said to-night, but I'd better work it out for myself." He sank down in his chair again, and then suddenly turned to me and flushed as he continued: "And to think that I've been imagining myself teaching you all this time! What a silly ass you must think me!"

"But you have been teaching me, Arthur," I replied gently. "You have taught me a lot about yourself, for one thing, which will make me jolly glad to have you as a Cubmaster in my district, if I take it on."

"Good of you to say that, sir," he murmured. "But I must be going now. Thanks most awfully for helping me like this."

I let him out, saw him down my garden-path to the gate, and returned to my den. And I thought, as I drank up the last of my cider and refilled my pipe, that Arthur Charles was a very nice boy indeed. His pride had received a nasty knock, and it had been a welcome surprise to me that he had accepted the situation in such a sporting spirit. I could not help but admire his determination to tackle the new idea in his own way, though at the same time I was a bit sorry for his attitude. To one of his youth and temperament it wasn't going to be easy; and, moreover, it threatened to seriously upset the second part of my little scheme.

However, I need not have worried about this; for the Fates, whom I had come to think were very much on my side, again came to the rescue.

5

I had been right in my surmise that the boy was not well when he came to see me that evening, for two days later I had occasion to call at his father's garage to order a further supply of oil and petrol, and heard all about it.

"Arthur's in bed with a chill," old Mr. Webb told me; "nothing much, but he'll stop in bed for a week if I have anything to do with it."

I expressed my sympathy, and promised to call in and see him that evening.

When I arrived I found Arthur Charles propped up in bed reading *The Scout* in a state of cheerful annoyance.

"Hullo, young man!" said I in greeting, "this is what comes of listening to that sermon I gave you the other evening. You must have a caught a chill while you were taking it all in."

He grinned at me and threw his paper aside.

"I don't think it's that, Major; but it's a bit of a bore, just as the schools have opened again and we can restart our meetings, isn't it?"

Like a good tactician I seized my opportunity. "Jolly hard luck," I agreed. "But your Cubs mustn't be disappointed. One of them stopped me in the High Street to-day, gave me a very nice salute, and wanted to know when they were going to start again. I said that I imagined it would be at once. So look here,

Arthur, you had much better let me take them for a couple of nights until you are fit to do so yourself. I've got to go off to Devonshire to see some relations in about ten days from now, and I shall be away for a month at least; but I could easily manage it between now and then, and it would be a useful part of my education. I was talking to Colonel Hartley the other day —he's D.C. for the northern end of the county, you know—and he said that he thought a certain amount of practical work was of the greatest value in a job of this kind. So just jot down what you would like me to do, some sort of a programme, and I'll carry on."

There was a slight pause while he weighed the matter in his mind; then he said: "It's jolly good of you, Major. I wanted to run the new idea on my own, but I don't want the kids let down, so if you really can manage it, I'll hand 'em over to you with pleasure and my blessing."

We then went into sundry details regarding the programme, and he promised to send notices round to the school and to the boys' parents calling a meeting for the following Tuesday.

It was then Saturday, and I thought, as I reviewed the matter that evening, that I had let myself in for it rather badly. However, it had to be gone through with now—I couldn't let the boy down after offering to take on the job—and besides, it fitted in with the scheme of things.

I felt that I could help in this way. Obviously it would have been difficult for Webb to change himself from the drill-sergeant into the romping playmate all at once. He was probably quite right in saying that his Cubs would think him daft, and it might possibly have the effect of increasing instead of diminishing their shyness of him. But if they themselves were to start the show and drag him into it, the solution of the problem would assume reasonable proportions.

So I argued to myself as I ran over Arthur's notes with the *Handbook*; and it was here where I felt that I could help him. It would, of course, mean drawing the boys themselves into the plot; but they would, after all, be unconscious agents, and I should be beyond the reach of possible reprisals by the time that the operations got to the really crucial stage.

I spent the rest of that evening recalling the few exciting incidents about real live tigers, snakes and bears which had come my way in India; for I felt, after my experience of Maybrick's Pack, that I should have to buy my way with some jolly good yarns before I fully gained the youngsters' confidence and co-operation.

During the next few days I often found myself chuckling at the spectacle of an elderly retired Indian Civil Servant plotting with thirty small boys for the reformation of their Cubmaster. It *was* rather ludicrous, if you come to think of it; but I believed that the end would justify the means, and at any rate I was willing to risk my own dignity in the experiment.

On the following Tuesday, therefore, I purposely arrived at the hut rather after the advertised time; for it was part of my plan to let my small allies get to the height of noise and excitement before I made a dramatic entry upon the scene.

They played up splendidly. A wonderful game was in full swing as I carefully reconnoitred the position through the window. Then I entered. The boys had been warned that I was to play substitute for their Cubmaster, and they evidently thought that my entrance would, as usual, signalise a return to strict normality. There was an abashed silence as they got up from various strange positions on the floor, gave me the Cub salute, and politely wished me "Good evening."

Seeing that a breezy self-assurance was the only way of saving a desperate situation, I called the Pack Leader—a merry little fellow of twelve—to me, and asked him what the game was, because I should like to play it too.

Jimmy looked up eagerly while his companions gathered round this strange new Cubmaster.

" Please, sir, we was playing Cowboys and Indians when you come in," he said.

" Righto ! " said I, " Cowboys and Indians it shall be. Which am I, a Cowboy or an Indian ? "

As there seemed to be a great amount of uncertainty on this point I took the initiative, and with a bound, really wonderful for one of my years, made for a corner of the room where I had noticed a couple of gym. mats. Behind these I barricaded myself, announced that I was the most bloodthirstiest of the fierce and wily Blackfeet tribe that had ever been known, and dared all the other tribes, with the Cowboys thrown in, to do their worst. Wasn't I the great Chief One-Eye of the Blackfeet ? I'd grind them all to little bits, take their scalps, and torture them horribly.

This threat was quite sufficient. With a bloodcurdling yell they were on me, my poor barricade was overwhelmed, and presently I found myself called upon to support the combined weight of as many of the young gentlemen as could find sitting or even standing room upon my person. It was a very hot game indeed, and as soon as I could get my breath I thought it politic to surrender.

" Well, now that you have got me," I gasped, " what is to be my awful fate ? At least I can die as a Chief of the Blackfeet should."

I really had no idea how a Chief of the Blackfeet was in the habit of dying, but it was certain to be death of a somewhat painful nature.

Up spake Jimmy, the Cowboy leader, as he flourished a lariat : " We're goin' to tie you to a stake, and burn you alive till you're dead . . . then we'll chop you up " —a suggestion which was received with acclamation by my foes and surprising fortitude by myself. Even such a terrible fate as this sounded cool in comparison with my present position.

I therefore allowed them to raise me from my recumbent attitude on the floor and securely bind me to an upright of the parallel-bars.

"Now that you've tied me up, what about a war-dance?" I suggested. "Also you'll want some fuel; I shan't burn well as I am."

The fuel consisted of any old thing to hand—two cricket-bats of battered appearance, some Indian clubs and a blanket or two forming a promising nucleus; and the war-dance began.

By this time we were all rather out of breath, so I thought that I would take a leaf out of Maybrick's book. My bonds were easily worked loose, and I suddenly cried, "Pack! Pack! Pack!" in the most approved manner.

Greatly to my relief the plan worked, and the boys quickly formed themselves into a circle, though not with the instant obedience and silence of the Wharton lot.

"That's splendid!" I remarked, as I took up my position in the centre. "Now we'll have the Grand Howl, and then I've got a list of things which your Cubmaster told me you must do."

The Howl was accomplished with the same perfection of timing as on my first visit, and we settled down to the routine part of the show. I can skip this. I kept to Webb's programme except for a variation in the usual physical jerks. Instead of these I taught them some simple P.T. games which I had seen played by the soldiers in training camps during the War. They were distinctly popular, and the boys would have liked to have gone on *ad lib.*; but it was getting late, and my chief job was as yet unaccomplished.

"Now," I said, as I fell them in again, "we are going to end up with a yarn. You'd like a yarn, wouldn't you?"

Chorus: "Yes-sir, please-sir."

And so I told them some very exciting things about real tigers and snakes and all sorts of wild animals, not forgetting the Bandarlog. I was delighted to find how easily I held them spellbound, breathless ; and it was quite a natural transition from the process of story-telling to the suggestion of their co-operation in my plan for helping Arthur Charles.

" And so, you see," I recounted, " the only thing they could do when they found that the tiger had fallen into their trap was to fetch ropes, make a big noose, and try to slip it over his head. They had been ordered by the Rajah to capture the tiger alive ; so they couldn't shoot him, and yet somehow or other they had to get him into the cage. And so they brought ropes, just like the one you tied me up with, only, of course, much stronger ; and they slipped one round his neck and another round his hind legs ; and then they drew the noose tight, so that they could pull him out of the pit and put him safely in the cage. Now I think you ought to learn a game something like that. Why not pretend one evening that your Cubmaster is a tiger struggling in a pit and that this room is the cage ? The bushes outside are the jungle, and that patch of grass half-way down the path is the pit. All you've got to do is to hide in the bushes and keep as quiet as mice. When he tumbles into the pit one of you must throw the noose over his head, and then you all rush out and capture him, and drag him to the cage and lock him in."

There ensued a breathless pause, while thirty pairs of round eyes gazed at me.

" Please, sir, we dursn't ; Mister Webb he mightn't like it," said Jimmy.

I had expected this argument, and was ready for it.

" Do you know, Jimmy," I replied very seriously, " I rather think that Mr. Webb would like it very much indeed ? He was telling me only the other evening how fond he was of games—only that you Cubs were such serious people that you wouldn't let him play any. You let *me* play, you know, but only because I asked you to ; and I enjoyed it very much indeed. I think you'll find that Mr. Webb will too."

They pondered this a bit. "Please, sir, p'raps he'll get dirty," was the next objection.

"Have you ever seen him in his pit at the garage?" I queried. "He's used to tumbling into pits there, and I don't think he really minds getting dirty."

This I found was a very useful line to take. None of them could deny that they had seen their Cubmaster very dirty indeed, even to the extent of oil all over his face and hair. And so at last it was agreed. After prayers and a final Howl we carefully rehearsed the whole incident, with myself as the tiger.

On the Friday evening we went through much the same programme, even to a further rehearsal; and on the Saturday I made good my escape to Devonshire.

It was nearly six weeks before I returned to Sledborough, and a week had elapsed after my return before I learnt the result of our dark scheming.

I was driving back about 7.30 in the evening from Adsleigh, where I had been paying an extended call, and my way through Sledborough lay past the Rectory grounds.

Some hundred yards short of the gate I had to pull up for a drove of cattle, and, while waiting for them to get safely past, I saw a sight which brought a pleasurable glow to my heart.

Behold Arthur Charles issuing from the Rectory gate in the midst of a throng of laughing, chattering Cubs. Even at that distance I could see that his face was aglow with fun and good-fellowship, very different to the expression of serious preoccupation with which he used to leave a Pack meeting.

I drove slowly on till I drew level with the cheery little crowd.

"Evening, Arthur," I cried. "You people are getting above yourselves, blocking the road like this. I shall have to start a rival Pack and set about you."

The boy grinned back, and (the sheer impudence of

it !) replied : " If you are really thinking of doing that, Major, you ought to come along and learn a thing or two from the 1st Sledborough—oughtn't he, Cubs ? "

" Yes-sir," they chorused.

" The Major would then see what a hopeless task he had, wouldn't he ? "

And " Yes-sir " laughed the little villains.

I assumed an air of mock dignity as I replied : " The great Chief of the Blackfeet Indians disdains your threat, and bids you farewell ! " and then I pressed the accelerator, and my horn echoed " Tut ! tut ! " as I moved on down the High Street.

But it was in no wise a peevish " Tut ! tut ! "—rather was it the kind of remark a man makes when he finds cause for a quiet satisfaction, not unmixed with a feeling of thankfulness at a difficult problem well and truly solved.

VII

OUR LOCAL ASSOCIATION

I

"TO be or not to be ?" was the question which I had asked myself many times during a period of two months following the episode of Arthur Charles Webb.

The question referred, of course, to Sir John Bingley's oft-repeated request that I should become District Commissioner of the Sledborough Association.

It may occur to many that, in view of the success of my initial experiment with Arthur Charles, I ought to have welcomed the opportunity of continuing a career which had opened with what I may be pardoned for calling a little victory of tact over susceptibility.

But there were difficulties—not in the game itself, for I was getting keener on that the more I saw of it—but in the personalities (or, shall I say, idiosyncrasies ?) of the good people who played it here in Sledborough.

Since the Webb affair I had visited all the Troops and Packs in the district, and had seen many different sides and also many different interpretations. Some were good, some were—well, not so good. But that didn't worry me, because the very elasticity of Scouting allows of somewhat diverse methods getting home in time.

What *did* worry me was the diversity of opinion amongst the adult members of the Association, and especially amongst those of them who belonged to the elected Committee.

Many of these good people did not appear to like

each other at all, and there went on a constant and most annoying undercurrent of intrigue founded upon nothing more substantial than these same little differences of opinion, and fanned. I regret to say, in some instances by a quite inexcusable petty jealousy.

Perhaps I had expected too much. When one comes fresh into a show like this, enthused by the possibilities, attracted by the delightful keenness of the boys, and hoping to find all connected with the game imbued with a like spirit, it is something of a shock to discover that, after all, they are really just like other people in their likes and dislikes, their little carping criticisms, and sometimes even their want of natural charity.

I suppose that one is apt to expect too much. But however that may be, here we were, a little community of some thirty souls in Sledborough, working towards a common goal, the helping of Sledborough's boys, using the most delightful means yet invented towards that end, and stating at intervals for all to hear that it was the spirit more than the material form of the thing which really counted. Yet it was the apparent lack of this same spirit which served to give the lie to our protestations.

I don't suppose that it was so in reality. Probably I was exaggerating the trouble in my own mind. I overlooked the fact—at least at first—that those who take part in these enterprises are generally highly strung and inclined also perhaps to be over-sensitive.

But there it was; and it was just this position of things in our Local Association which gave me pause.

I could see that the office of District Commissioner was one which would require infinite tact; and really I was not certain that I possessed a sufficiency of that useful commodity.

I expressed this view to dear old Sir John, the County Commissioner, when I lunched with him at Albuck Manor on a day following an especially acrimonious meeting of the Executive Committee.

Perhaps " acrimonious " is again an exaggeration (I am beginning to think that I may be inclined that way), but I remember that I left the meeting that night feeling somewhat depressed and disappointed.

Scantling had been difficult. Scantling was a big butcher in the town (we all got our meat from him), and he was also Chairman of the Sledborough Local Association.

He was certainly a better butcher than he was a Chairman. I had early summed him up as a man with big feet and a small mind. But that was very likely because he appeared to resent any kind of interference on my part. Quite right, I dare say, from his point of view; for, after all, I was a newcomer, and at that time only a co-opted member of his Committee, and quite possibly I was wanting in tact; but the man annoyed me.

And so you see that at the top of the tree of trouble there were the Chairman and the prospective District Commissioner at loggerheads with one another—not a propitious start.

And that evening there had been trouble about Miss Wild, one of the Cubmasters and a person of strong and rather overbearing character. Miss Wild had lodged a formal complaint against Miss Lidger, another Cubmaster, whom she accused of poaching in her preserves—to wit, gaining a recruit from a street which was stated to be in Miss Wild's area. The subsequent discussion about this street had been heated and wanting in dignity; and I had asked, quite meekly I hope: " Does it really matter so long as the boy joins one Pack or the other? "

And then I had been rebuked by Scantling in what I considered a very tactless way:

" It matters very much indeed, Major Caryll. It is of the utmost importance that Troops and Packs should keep strictly to their prescribed areas, and I consider that Miss Wild's protest is quite justified." Pompous ass!

And then, after all, they had discovered, on reference

to a previous minute, that the street in question had been solemnly transferred some months before, and that therefore Miss Lidger had been quite within her rights in accepting the small boy; and I might add that the small boy had shown sound common sense in selecting Miss Lidger; but that's neither here nor there.

Miss Wild, however, asked for a reconsideration of the minute in question, and there had been more unnecessary discussion. But finally a Sub-Committee was appointed to go into the whole subject of boundaries, and the incident closed for the moment.

But that was not all. Apparently old Nangarrow's band practice had caused offence to a neighbouring prayer-meeting, and a letter from the Reverend James Maddox was read out. Evidently this gentleman did not believe in Scouts—he confessed, in fact, that he knew little about them, except that they made a most unholy noise and upset his prayer-meetings. He concluded a long letter by saying that if Scouts were as bad as they sounded, the sooner they closed down the better it would be for everyone concerned.

I couldn't help feeling a certain sympathy with the Reverend James. I myself don't much like a single bugle, even if well played, and I can quite imagine that a number of them blown incorrectly and out of tune (Scout buglers, I find, have this distressing habit) would be most upsetting to any meeting, prayer or otherwise.

Old Nangarrow was quite sensible about it, as I had found him to be about most things if tackled in the right way. He agreed that they *had* made rather a noise, and said that he was considering the question of doing away with all but one or two of his instruments of torture. He also suggested that he should apologise in person to the Reverend James; and all would have been well if it hadn't been for that silly young ass, Billingham.

Billingham was all right in his way—very keen and capable up to a point—but he was also excessively young.

Not that I consider excessive youth to be a crime—far from it. Being of an advanced middle age myself, I envy excessive youth. But Billingham was sometimes tactlessly young, and also he happened to be the only Scoutmaster for miles around who had done a course at Parkwell.

That again was all to the good, if he hadn't promptly fallen into the habit of thrusting Parkwell forward into all our discussions, and thereby making it appear that we poor people, who had not been there, really knew nothing about Scouting at all.

As I have said, it would have been all right in this case if it hadn't been for Billingham. Old Nangarrow's idea of an apology had been well received, and I had offered to lead the Reverend James by the hand and show him that there really was more in Scouting than mere noise—in fact, Scantling was peering through his glasses at the next item on the agenda—when the young ass got up, looked pointedly at Nangarrow, and said: "Mr. Chairman, isn't it about time that this Committee went into the whole question of bands and bugles. Now at Parkwell——" And then, of course, the fat was properly in the fire.

Nangarrow was quite quiet about it, but I could see that the old man was really angry, and at that moment just about hated Billingham and his Parkwell.

"I have been nearly fourteen years in the Scout Movement, Mr. Chairman," he began—"in fact, I was Scoutmaster of the 1st Sledborough when Mr. Billingham was in the nursery, where some of us think he ought to be still. I've never been to Parkwell, but I've talked to quite a number who have, and I have no doubt at all that it is a fine place. But one thing I *am* certain of is that they don't encourage people who have had the luck to do a course there to come back and 'Parkwell this' and 'Parkwell that' all the time. Some of us may be old-fashioned—I dare say we are—but when we started with the boys before ever Parkwell was thought of, what was the first thing we did ? Well, we bought *Scouting for Boys* (Mr. Billingham may have heard of it), and we read it, and we are trying to run our Troops according to it. Mind you, I've nothing to say against Parkwell—it's a fine thing for them what can afford the time and money—but I should like to tell Mr. Billingham this, which he can put in his pipe and smoke : if he goes on Parkwelling us any more, it's not going to make it easier to get fellows to go there."

Nangarrow sat down amidst murmurs of applause (Billingham wasn't very popular), and I thought it an opportune moment to pour oil on the troubled waters, in spite of Scantling remarking, " Is it necessary to prolong this discussion, Major ? "

" I think that it is, Mr. Chairman," I replied ; " but I promise you that I will not be long. I just want to ask everyone a simple question : What are we out for ? We have been sitting here for over an hour, and, as far as I can see, the only constructive bit of business we have done is the appointment of a Sub-Committee to undo the work done by another Sub-Committee years ago. I sometimes wonder whether we know what we really are out for, or, knowing, care, so long as we can turn these meetings into a bear-garden. I haven't been in the Movement long, as you all know, and I doubt if I shall be in it much longer " (murmurs of " No, no ! ")—" that is to say, if we cannot try to bring more of the spirit of the thing into this room. What, after all, *are* we out for ? As I take it, it is the training of the boys in unselfishness, kindliness, friendship, loyalty—all those delightful attributes which go to the making of a good citizen.

" If that really is so, surely we can only do it by the personal example of those who have taken on the responsibility of leadership. I know that it is very impertinent of me to talk like this to people who have been Scouting for more years than I have been months or even weeks, but the County Commissioner has honoured me by asking me to become your District Commissioner. If you don't want me, by all means continue the bear-garden business ; if you do, I must really ask that a spirit more in accordance with the ideals of Scouting shall prevail amongst us in future."

It was a long speech for me, and I sat down rather red in the face, fearing that possibly I had put the matter too strongly for a first dose ; and this appeared to be Scantling's opinion, for he was pleased to be sarcastic.

" Very interesting, Major ; and I am sure that we are all glad to have your opinion of us. But personally I wasn't aware of any bear-garden business, as you are pleased to call it—not that I know exactly what you mean by a bear-garden. And now shall we go on to the next item, the Competition for the Smithson Trophy."

I couldn't stand this sort of thing from anyone—least of all from Scantling. I got to my feet again.

" Excuse me, Mr. Chairman," said I, while he frowned at me over his spectacles, " but I've still got something to say. Since I was first invited to your Committee I have had the pleasure of visiting every Troop and Pack in the district ; and when I think of those pleasant little visits and the keenness of the youngsters, I feel that perhaps I have been a little hasty in what I said just now.

" There seem to me to be many methods in Scouting by which we can attain the common goal, and it is probably just this divergency of method which causes occasional ill-feeling. Mr. Nangarrow, for instance, stands for one method ; Billingham for another. Isn't it possible that they may both be successful with the boys ? And one other thing. A good deal has been said this evening about Parkwell, and I don't wish to add to it except to suggest that it might be a good thing if someone else were to do a course at that institution, if only for the purpose of keeping a certain young gentleman in order." (General laughter, in which Billingham joined.)

" I will go a step farther, and I hereby promise you

that on the first possible occasion I myself will do a course at Parkwell." (Cheers.)

"Wait a moment, please; there is a condition—namely, that you on your part will strive to make these meetings of ours more like the happy evenings we spend with the boys, where serious work, plenty of fun, and, above all, the happy bond of a common object shall be combined."

I sat down again amidst quite a little ovation, led by Nangarrow and Maybrick, and the agenda was concluded in a happier spirit.

But in spite of that I had gone home in a rather depressed frame of mind, which was not in any way lightened by the company of Scantling for part of the way. Our conversation was brief—one couldn't converse for long with Scantling—but I felt bound to apologise to him in some measure for what he might have considered a usurpation of his authority; and the man had the impudence to agree with me.

"Well, yes, if you care to put it in that way, it was," he said; "but we'll let it pass this time—eh?"

Let it pass indeed! I felt like kicking Scantling, but that would have been hardly in accordance with the high plane of my recent public utterances. So I agreed that we would let it pass, and somewhat abruptly bade him "Good-night."

Later in the evening little Maybrick came in to see me and to smoke a soothing pipe, and I poured my woes into his sympathetic ears.

"Bless you!" he said, "don't mind them. They are all right at the bottom, and I don't think that they hate each other as much as it would appear. You were really first-rate, Caryll—just the tonic we need." And then he looked at me with a twinkle in his eyes as he went on: "What's all this nonsense about your not taking on the job? You've simply got to do it. Don't you like Scouting, man? Of course you do. What about the boys? Isn't it just *the* show for them? Of course it is, and you know it, Caryll. And you are going to say 'Yes' to old Sir John to-morrow—now aren't you?"

But I was not to be drawn. I said that I wanted to sleep on it and talk it over with the old boy to-morrow—seek inspiration from his lunch, and so on; and Maybrick took the hint and bade me "Good-night."

2

At one o'clock the following day I found myself looking at old Sir John across the gleaming silver on his famous mahogany table.

I had left home half an hour earlier with the fixed intention of asking for more time—a determination which I carried with me into the dining-room and jealously guarded until lunch was over.

I remember little about the meal itself—I don't much mind what I eat—except that there was some wonderful old Grave Supérieur, one of those wines which simply melt away in the mouth. But that has nothing to do with my tale, just as I affirm it had nothing to do with my final acceptance.

I ought to describe Sir John, because it was the man himself and his courtly old-world charm of manner which really did the trick. He was seventy-eight, I believe, but he didn't look it, and of that delightful type which one finds scattered at intervals throughout the length and breadth of the country. A large landowner, he had been impoverished by the conscientious acceptance of the responsibilities of his position, a keen sportsman in spite of his years, and one who had spent his life in the quiet service of his fellow-men.

Sir John did not profess to know much about Scouting, explaining that it had come too late in life for him; but he had realised its worth from the first, and had said more than once that the post of County Commissioner was one of the last of his public duties he wished to give up.

In fact, he spoke to me about this during lunch.

" I'm an old man, Caryll," he added, " and I can't expect to go on much longer. It's a job for you youngsters, and I hope that you are ready to take on the Sledborough district now. I know that there are difficulties, but you'll get over 'em all right, and I want to feel that the movement is in good hands all over the county before I obey my doctor-man and hand it over to someone else."

" I appreciate the compliment, Sir John," I replied, " but I came out here intending to ask for a little longer to think things over. The fact is, the boys are all right ; so is the game—you know what I feel about that. It's the people who run it in Sledborough who are my trouble. Some of them are first-rate—Maybrick, Nangarrow and young Webb, for instance—but the feeling is all wrong somehow ; they are so infernally touchy—seem to think more of their blessed rights and the other fellow's wrongs than of what lies behind the whole thing. I confess that I'm a disappointed man, Sir John. Our meeting last night was a regular bear-garden, and I took an opportunity of telling 'em so, and got snubbed by Scantling for my pains. Incidentally I nearly kicked him afterwards."

" Wish you had quite," chuckled the old boy. " I never liked the man, but he sells good meat," he added, rather irrelevantly I thought.

" I dare say that his meat's all right," I rejoined, " but why in thunder was he ever made Chairman ? "

" That's a matter of old history. Poor Brown was responsible, I suppose, but it seems to have missed fire rather badly. The fact is, Caryll," he went on, " there has never been anyone at the head of affairs in Sledborough who has had any idea of running a show like this. Brown himself was very little good, though I believe that he tried his best. But he hadn't the requisite personality—which you have."

" You make it very difficult for me to refuse when you talk like that," I said.

Sir John smiled gently at me as he led the way into his den.

"I mean to make it difficult for you to refuse, Caryll," he replied. "Tell me, when you talked to them like a father last night, was there any appreciable lightening of the atmosphere? I rather gather from Maybrick that there was. Oh yes, the Reverend Thomas rushed out here to see me at eleven o'clock this morning, and told me all about it. What he said was complimentary to you. Don't you think, Caryll, that we want to look rather beyond all these little surface difficulties and get at the broader aspect of the thing? It is so essentially good, and we can't afford to waste good things nowadays."

Of course, the end of it was that I gave my consent, simply because I couldn't do anything else. The gallant old gentleman had made me feel like a petulant child, and I told him so.

"You are not that," he said, as I got into my car and switched on the self-starter; "but possibly it might be a good thing to treat some of the members of your Committee in that light. Be a father to them, Caryll—a helpful, kindly, but firm father, especially to my estimable butcher."

"I'll spank him if I get the chance," I retorted savagely; and then let in the clutch and went home.

3

Three weeks later my warrant as District Commissioner was solemnly presented to me by Sir John himself after a Church Parade of the whole Association. He made a very kindly little speech, and then the boys gave me three cheers as if they meant it.

I flatter myself that they did, for I had paid many informal visits to their clubrooms just to see how the game was being played. Sometimes it was difficult to make these visits as informal as I could have wished, although I always made a point of asking permission to come and of requesting at the same time that everything should go on as usual.

Old Nangarrow, for instance, treated me like a victorious Field-Marshal : Troop drawn up in line, General Salute (quite deafening and indifferently played), and to my horror a reporter from the Sledborough *Argus* to record what I said in my " few words." I'm afraid that I was not what he would describe as good copy ; I didn't even commence, " Scouts of the 1st Sledborough Troop," and then proceed to tell them that they were the best ever ; nor, I regret to say, did I find it in me to congratulate the band upon their appalling noise.

After inspecting the turn-out, which was really very good, I asked Nangarrow to let the boys sit round in a circle while I told them stories. Then I taught them a new game which I had often seen played by native boys in my Indian district ; and after that, when the atmosphere had lost all its formality, saw them do some work by Patrols. Old Nangarrow, rather horrified at first, ended up by joining in the fun like a boy, and was good enough to ask me to come again as soon as I could. So I had got to know the boys and realise their keenness, and, of course, it made me all the keener myself—you can't help it if you take Scouting in the right way.

But all the same I was not quite certain that my visits were so welcome with one or two of the Scoutmasters. Perhaps they thought that I wanted to interfere ; perhaps I was over-sensitive, and it was just a way they had. But the net result was a lack of spontaneity on my part and a certain frigidness on theirs. However, there were only two who seemed like this, and I made up my mind that time would probably alter their attitude.

Scantling wasn't present at the Church Parade ; I neither expected nor wanted him ; and I noticed also that he made no reference to my becoming District Commissioner at the next meeting of the Committee.

I don't think Scantling liked me. I know that I didn't like him, and I agreed with Maybrick that somehow or other he would have to go. Finally he did ; but that's another story altogether.

In spite of the Chairman, our meetings improved wonderfully, both in tone and in the value of the business done. I take no credit to myself for this, except that I did two things which may have helped matters.

There was an old barn at the bottom of my little garden. It was in quite good repair, and one day it occurred to me to turn it into a clubroom for a Troop and Pack at my end of the town who had only a schoolroom for their meeting place. I also suggested to the Committee that it should be used for their meetings as well.

Scantling was against this—he would be—but only on what he called the " general grounds of inaccessibility " ; and when I suavely pointed out that the trams came to within three hundred yards of my gate, and that the room at the " Swan " was costing us ten shillings a time, he subsided with a bad grace, and my offer was accepted.

I took a lot of trouble with that room, and really got it rather nice, with the help of the boys. We gave it a thorough clean out, washed it a light green, put in a good stove and a proper door in place of the original big folding ones, and I then made it over to the 8th Sledborough for four nights a week.

The other thing I did was to institute weekly suppers on Sunday evenings at my cottage, to which I invited members of the Association two at a time. I think that they liked coming ; I know that I enjoyed having them —and what nice people they were when we met like that !

Miss Wild and Miss Lidger were one pair. You may think that this was tactless, but as a matter of fact it worked very well. They didn't really dislike one another at all, and anyhow we never had any more trouble about that street.

One day I invited Scantling and young Billingham. Please don't imagine that I was showing a proper spirit towards Scantling in so doing, because I knew very well that he wouldn't come—he always played pool at the Swan Hotel on Sunday evenings—but I felt that I must at least give him the chance, and I coupled him with Billingham because I wanted to get that young man to myself for a quiet talk. Scantling played the game for once, and declined with thanks, and Billingham duly turned up alone.

I liked young Billingham really, and he was certainly very keen on what he called the spirit of the backwoods. He had never been to any backwoods, but he had read every book within reach upon Nature-lore and tribal customs, and his imagination was receptive.

Of course, I took the opportunity of tackling him on the subject of his want of tact over that business of the bugles ; but at first he didn't show much penitence.

" Sorry, Major, but you know old ' Dam-narrow ' is rather——"

And then I had to cut him short.

" Look here, young man," said I, " I really can't have you taking the name of a brother-Scout in vain like that."

And he replied with a grin : " I suppose it's not good form, but it *does* describe him rather well, doesn't it ? "

" It's not only bad form, but it's untrue," I retorted ; and then proceeded to give him a bad ten minutes. I know that he was my guest, but he had simply asked for it, and this sort of thing had to be stopped.

" Look here, Billingham," I went on ; " quite apart from what you said just now being untrue and bad form, Nangarrow happens to be a friend of mine, and incidentally he is old enough to be your father. You are young, Billingham—twenty-two, isn't it ?—and you are jolly lucky to be young ; but youth and book-knowledge are not everything, nor is a course at Parkwell. I went down there myself the other day, and I thought it was absolutely first-rate ; but, after all, the course they give you is only a demonstration of the Chief's ideas as given in *Scouting for Boys*, which is just what Nangarrow goes on himself. I'm going to do a course in the summer, because I think that it will do me a lot of good, but it certainly will not give me the right to criticise Nangarrow. Do you know anything of his history, by the way ? "

Billingham shook his head.

" Well, then, I'll tell it you ; it may do you good. You and the rest of the town know Nangarrow as a man who keeps a small tobacconist's shop in the High Street and runs a Troop of Scouts. But he is more than that. About forty years ago Nangarrow started life as a drummer-boy in his father's old regiment, and by sheer merit rose to be Corporal, Sergeant, Quartermaster-Sergeant, and finally Quartermaster, and retired with the rank of Captain.

" Long before you were thought of, my lad, he was impressing his own fine character on young army recruits, just as he is to-day on his Boy Scouts. You never hear him talk much about himself, do you ? He doesn't din into our ears what they did in the army, and I've never got him to tell me the story of his D.C.M. at Spion Kop. But his record and those two rows of medal-ribbons speak for him quite eloquently enough. Stated briefly, Nangarrow belongs to one of the finest types of men I know—the best class of British N.C.O."

Billingham fidgeted about a bit with his pipe, and then said :

" Yes, I know, Major ; but look at his band and all that drill, and those awful breeches he wears ! "

" My dear boy, what on earth has that got to do with it ? I know that he doesn't wear shorts—I don't suppose that he ever will—but it isn't shorts that make a Scoutmaster, Billingham. Personally I like them, but they are rather a new fashion for men, and some people are a bit shy about it. And as for his band, you heard what he said about doing away with most of it. I wonder if you realise what that means to a man who has spent all the best years of his life within sound of a bugle ? You are quite wrong, too, in thinking that he does nothing but drill. His Troop happens to be the best turned-out in the district, and I know that they click their heels a bit, but they are jolly good at their Patrol work all the same, and can put up a first-rate Gym. show."

"Yes, but games are better than all that Gym.," Billingham objected.

"If you ask me," I replied, "I should say that most boys can do with a bit of both—and Nangarrow's Troop have both. Have you ever been to one of his meetings?"

"Can't say that I have."

"Well, if you ever do, you will find that he can play a game with the best of them. Bit stiff in the joints, of course, but the more credit to him that he should do it at all."

Billingham looked at me doubtfully. "Do you mean to say that he tumbles about on the floor and all that?" he asked.

"I don't suppose that he makes a habit of it," I replied with a smile, "but I'd back him to do it when occasion arises. What's more, I'd back him to put you over his knee and spank you with one hand tied behind his back."

Billingham got rather red in the face as I went on: "And I'm not sure that it wouldn't be rather a good thing if he did."

"Hang it all, Major! I'm sorry if—— "

"Hold hard," I interrupted; "I haven't quite finished yet. There is another thing about Nangarrow which you may have noticed, and that is the way in which his older boys stick to the Troop; he practically never loses a boy until he has to go for some reason or other unconnected with Scouting. Have you ever seen his letter-book, as he calls it?"

Billingham looked puzzled. "His letter-book? No, what's that?" he asked.

"Nangarrow's letter-book," I replied, "is a rather remarkable document; but I gather that he doesn't show it to everyone. I've seen it, and so has Maybrick, and it consists of a big scrap-book crammed with letters from old Scouts of his Troop written from all over the world. They are delightful letters, Billingham, the sort of letters which must make Scouting seem very well worth while to old Nangarrow. Some day you may have a book like that yourself. I hope you will, because I can't think of any better reward for years of work and devotion. Nangarrow was having supper here last Sunday, and we were talking about you."

"Good Lord!" said Billingham. "I bet he said some nasty things."

"Nangarrow isn't that sort," I replied rather sharply. "On the contrary, he said some very nice things about you—praised your keenness and your jolly little Troop, and told me what a first-rate camp you had last Whitsun."

The boy got to his feet with a very red face indeed.

"Oh, I say, Major, did he really? And here I've been slanging him all this time. What a cad you must think me!"

"I don't think so a bit, Billingham, or you wouldn't be having supper here. And perhaps it wasn't quite fair of me to let out at you like this all at once. But I've been trying to point out just two things. The first is that, in spite of Parkwell, you have still something left to learn; and the second is that old Nangarrow is one of those delightful people—a very good Scout."

Young Billingham got up again to take his departure, and I must say that he showed up at his best when he confessed on my doorstep: "You've taught me a jolly good lesson, Major. I'll go round and see Nangarrow as soon as I can and tell him how sorry I am that I've been such a cub."

"I shouldn't do that," I said as we shook hands; "it might embarrass the old boy. Just drop in casually one evening and see his Troop, and then ask him to come and see yours. Later on you shall both come to supper here; and perhaps, if you are very good, Billingham, you may see that letter-book yet."

And that was how another little breach was healed.

4

Early in the summer we held a Jamboree. There was a certain amount of difficulty about it.

To begin with, Scantling didn't like the idea, possibly because it was my proposal. He doubted whether we could put up a good enough show, and also urged that it would interfere with the routine work of the Troops. He got quite angry when I said that this was just what I wanted it to do ; and my remark also caused a certain amount of surprise to the rest of the Committee. But I explained what I meant in a few words.

"I don't agree with the Chairman," was my rather tactless beginning. "In the first place I have seen quite enough of the Troops and Packs to convince me that we could put up quite a good show ; secondly, I feel that it would be a good thing for the whole Association to pull together in a common effort. We are rather apt to get into a groove, and that is just what makes me think that a change from the ordinary routine Scouting would do us all good. Again, there has never been such a thing in Sledborough since the movement started here, and in consequence people don't really know what we are up to. Lots of them probably think the same as did the Reverend James Maddox until I took him round and showed him the boys at work. I believe that we could fill the Town Hall for two nights running, and get some much-needed cash for the Association funds. I beg to propose that a Jamboree be held, and that a Sub-Committee be formed for the purpose of working out details."

As a matter of fact, I hadn't sprung the thing on them suddenly, but had talked most of them round some time before ; and my proposal was carried after considerable, but I am glad to say friendly, discussion.

The Jamboree was a great success, as I was sure that it would be ; but I haven't space to tell you much about it here—in fact, I only mentioned it at all in order to introduce to your notice the Hon. Bertie Challoner.

Bertie was some sort of a faint connection of mine, and he lived three miles away from Sledborough, at the Tower House, up on Wrexford Downs. You probably know Wrexford Downs, a great place for training race-horses—but that fact is only incidental to my story.

What *does* matter is that I got Bertie to open the Jamboree on the second day (old Sir John did this, of course, on the first), because the Challoner family between them owned most of the town—in fact, I was one of Bertie's tenants.

He made an excellent little speech, showing a quite amazing ignorance of Scout matters; but fortunately he didn't say anything very dreadful, and his mistakes gave me an excuse for leading him round like a father, and explaining just where he had gone wrong. I am very fond of Bertie Challoner, and I deem him worthy of a brief description.

Aged thirty-two, and the possessor of a game leg as the result of a motor smash, he couldn't get about very much; but he did a bit of racing, trained his own horses (quite successfully, I believe), and was immensely rich.

Everybody liked him, but everybody agreed that there were two faults in his make-up. One was that he took things up violently for a time, tried to do them better than anyone else (which wasn't difficult, with his money), and then dropped them for something else. That was the first thing. The other was a curious and rather absurd little habit he had of putting the word "what" into almost every sentence without any real reason or desire for a reply. Hardly a fault, perhaps, but annoying at times.

Well, as I have said, Bertie Challoner opened our Jamboree on the second day, and I talked to him like a father about Scouts. I could see that he was both surprised and interested, especially as he watched the boys sing, and dance, and act, and examined all the wonderful things they had made.

But I never anticipated the sequel. It was a distinct shock to me when I got the following letter from him about two months later:

DEAR GEORGE [it ran],

I liked that Scout show of yours no end. Just what we want these days. I thought quite a lot for me when I got back home after making a fool of myself on the platform. By the way, I never thanked you for letting me down so easily; you called me a silly ass in a way which would do justice to the best traditions of the Diplomatic Corps. Well, George, when I got back I had a meeting of all the boys in Wrexford—most of 'em stable lads, as you know—and we decided to start a Troop. There was no one else to do Scoutmaster, so I've taken on the job myself. I'm building a room for them down by the Old Pool, and all their uniforms arrived last week. They look top-hole. Rather a tasty thing in scarves, purple and gold—my racing colours, you know. What I want you to do, old boy, is to come up here one day soon and inspect 'em. You will have a chance of telling me how nice I look in shorts.

Yours ever,

BERTIE.

I took up my pen and replied as follows:

DEAR BERTIE,

I had no idea when I invited you to open our Jamboree that it would have such tragic consequences. I'll do what I can for you, and only hope that things are not as bad as they seem. If you are coming in for the Grammar School meeting next Saturday, lunch with me at the Club, and we'll talk about it.

Yours more in sorrow than anger,

GEORGE.

I should perhaps explain that light badinage of this nature was the ordinary medium of conversation between

Bertie and myself. But all the same I was a bit worried. The Scout Movement is far too important a matter to be used as a temporary plaything by rich young men with nothing better to do for the moment, and I found it hard to believe that it could be anything but a passing obsession to one of Bertie's volatile mind.

So after lunch on Saturday we repaired to a quiet corner of the smoking-room, and there I had it out with him.

"Look here, Bertie," I began, "what's all this about your starting a Troop? You'll get sick of it in three months, drop it like a hot penny, and I shall probably never get Scouts going in Wrexford again. You had much better leave it alone, and I'll see if I can't send out a couple of Rovers to get the thing on its legs."

"Too late, George, old man," he replied; "hounds are in full cry. Building the room—we meet in the Riding School at present—got our uniforms and all complete—what?"

"It's not a bit too late," I retorted, "and all is *not* complete. What about your warrant and the registration of your Troop? Has it occurred to you, most excellent Bertie, that the Local Association can refuse to recommend both?"

Bertie smiled a superior smile. "Better let 'em try," he said. "If they do, I shall give notice to quit to their revered Commissioner—what?"

"I don't think that would worry them very much," I said. "But honestly, Bertie, are you serious about the show? It might be the making of you if you were. If I thought for a moment that you *were* serious, I'd take the risk and even intercede with my Committee on your behalf."

Bertie gave what is generally described as a grim chuckle, but he looked as solemn as it is possible for him to look as he assured me that this was going to be the one great thing in his life, or words to that effect.

"I'm serious enough about it, George—what? I mean to say, it's a jolly good show and all that—saving of the country—what ? And I believe I'll make a tip-top Scoutmaster. Aunt Emma always tells me that I've wanted an aim in life—and you have, too, for that matter. Also, I like the village boys—always got on well with them. But they're impudent young blighters. What do you think they did at our last meeting—what ? "

I assured him that I couldn't even hazard a guess, but that it was probably something pretty awful.

" Well, when I arrived rather late, I found 'em laughing and chattering all together in a corner of the school. One young imp was writing down a list of their names and another was mixing up slips of paper in a Scout hat. It took me a bit of time to tumble to the game, but I found it out at last—what ? "

" Well ? " I queried.

" Impudent young blighters were having a sweepstake on the number of ' what's ' I was going to say in the course of the evening."

It was my turn for a grim chuckle, and Bertie went on : " I shouldn't have minded that so much if only they'd been sportsmen enough to let me take a ticket."

" My dear Bertie," I explained gently, " if you are going to run a Scout Troop, I would suggest that there are better methods of character training than the encouragement of sweepstakes."

" Agreed," said Bertie ; " and seriously, George, I'm going through with the job—I'm dead keen on it. I've read *Scouting for Boys* and *Aids to Scoutmastership* and one or two others, and Scouting's just what we want in Wrexford—beats footer and the Stable Lads' Club to a frazzle—what ? "

I agreed somewhat doubtfully.

" You know, I suppose, that you have to be on probation for a bit before you can have a warrant ? And for Heaven's sake don't go and spend a lot of money on them."

Bertie looked distressed.

" What's the good of having it if one can't do a thing

like this well ?" he replied. "The boys must have a clubroom and uniforms and tents—what ?"

"Just so," said I ; "but all the Troops in Sledborough have got them, and I don't think that any of the Scoutmasters, as far as I am aware, possess an income of thirty-five thousand a year. You go home and read *Scouting for Boys* again, and I'll come up next Thursday to see how you are getting on."

Bertie said that Thursday would suit him ; and then we both adjourned to the Grammar School meeting.

5

It was with grave misgivings that I drove over to the Tower House on the appointed evening. I started off with the full intention of being the stern, implacable guardian of the whole Scout Brotherhood against its frivolous misuse at the hands of the Hon. Bertie Challoner.

But I must also confess that, deep down in my soul, was just a suspicion that I should find this most correct attitude extremely difficult to keep up.

Sternness, implacability, virtuous indignation, had a way of rolling off his honourable back like water off a duck, and I may tell you in confidence that the grim set of my mouth (good phrase, that) relaxed appreciably directly I espied him waving cheerily to me from the carved portal of his ancient keep.

Snadwell the butler, and a family retainer of whom I stood in some awe, was standing in the dim background of the Great Hall regarding Bertie's back view with an expression of sad deference, as who should say : "I've watched over 'im from when 'e was so 'igh ; I served 'is father before 'im ; but never did I think as I'd live to see the day when a full-grown Challoner was to go skippin' about in bare knees and a Scout 'at !"

Of course, Snadwell may not have been thinking anything of the sort ; he may have been merely lamenting the fact that it would be harder than ever now to preserve the proper *morale* and discipline of a great house—which had entertained royalty in its time—amongst the small army of men-servants whose main job in life was to see that his master was fed, clothed (decently), and otherwise made comfortable.

However that may be, whatever the thoughts in the mind of the impeccable Snadwell, the fact remains that Bertie certainly did look well in his Scout kit, complete down to the ominous knife at his hip ; and the boys looked as smart as paint in the most expensive uniforms that money could buy.

But there were too many of them—about forty—and early in the proceedings I spotted two or three who were quite evidently there for purposes of ragging alone. I must admit, however, that Bertie had a certain way with them which I liked, and he had chosen his Patrol Leaders with care. He had also, I learnt, worked up the Tenderfoot Tests with them privately, and they appeared quite capable of teaching the others. Bertie, in fact, apart from the size of his Troop and the free gift of their uniforms before they had earned the right to wear them, had evidently studied the books to some advantage, and had done his best to start away right.

I confess that I was surprised at him that evening. I had always known him as a jolly good fellow and a sportsman, but he came out now in quite a new light. He was *bon camarade* without being frivolous, and quietly firm when occasion demanded, and I could see that he was popular with the boys.

I suppose that it was that instinctive something which is said to come from a long line of ancestors born to command which did the trick, but it was certainly there in Bertie, and I had not realised the fact.

Of course, there were troubles ahead—too big a Troop for one thing, all that splash and display paid for out of his own pocket, and then that room he was building. But I was beginning to think that he might weather the storms and come through into calm water, if only he stuck it. A mighty big " if," thought I, knowing (or thinking that I knew) my Bertie.

When we had watched the Tenderfoot Tests, a game or two, and some stave drill and tent-pitching on the tan floor of the Riding School, Bertie left the Troop in charge of Crompton, and took me off to see the room. Crompton, I should explain, was his second chauffeur and prospective A.S.M., and incidentally an old Scout of Nangarrow's—nice boy, who would possibly be able to carry on if and when his master got sick of it.

The room had only just begun to appear above the ground, but Bertie proudly produced all the plans, and was, I am afraid, a bit riled at my criticism of the needless expenditure proposed.

" Of course, it will be a gorgeous place," I agreed, " but is it necessary to have a separate gymnasium, hot baths, and a complete cinema installation, not to speak of a Radiogram?"

" No, I suppose it isn't *necessary*, any more than it was necessary for an interfering old blighter of a Commissioner to come up here and try to upset all my plans."

" Don't be a silly ass, Bertie," I replied. " I'm only doing it for your good, my son—and incidentally for the good of Scouting in my district. Have you thought of one possible result of all this lavishness ? I suppose that you wouldn't like your Troop to be known to all and sundry as the 1st Wrexford Spoonfeds or the Bradbury Boys ; nor would you like someone to come up here on a dark night and paint ' All is not gold that glitters ' on the door of your Scout Palace.

" After all, Bertie, I've got to think of the rest. There is a Troop in the town so poor that they can only afford to heat their clubroom every other meeting. On the cold nights they have to spend the time in active exercise to keep themselves warm. Yet that little Troop has got a spirit which couldn't be bought with ten thousand golden sovereigns."

Bertie was studying the plans in his hand with a

rather rueful countenance, and I had it in my heart to be sorry for him—or rather I should have been if it had been anyone else—for I was really beginning to believe that there was something behind his apparent keenness this time. It was just this fact, though, which made me anxious to rub in what I wanted to convey to his intelligence, at present evidently somewhat doubtful where the finer ethics of Scouting were concerned.

" Another point, Bertie," I continued, therefore: " do you really think that boys appreciate having money spent on them like this? They will be quite excited about it until the novelty wears off, no doubt, but to my mind there are two things essential to real success in running Scouts. The first is a good Scoutmaster, and the second letting the boys feel that the Troop is as much their concern as his. Not only must they help to run the show, but they must help to pay for it. That's the only way to get the right spirit and build up a tradition. Don't you think I'm right? Scouting is a game, Bertie, but it must be played to rules like any other. You've broken one already by getting your fellows into uniform before passing their Tenderfoot Tests and taking the Promise. As long as they don't wear it outside no harm will be done, and I dare say that you'll get them through in another few meetings, but this self-government business *is* important."

" I see what you mean, George, and I suppose I did the wrong thing in not consulting you first—what? But hang it all, I've ordered the whole show now—signed the contract and told 'em to go ahead. All the foundations are in and the walls sprouting up. What the deuce am I to do?"

It was then that I made a rash suggestion; but I saw that it was up to me to suggest something.

" Why not hold a Garden Fête to wipe off the debt?"

" All very well; but there won't be any debt to wipe off. Try another. And what's a Garden Fête got to do with the boys, anyhow?"

" I see your first point, Bertie," I replied, " but nobody need know how much you are spending on the room, and you can leave the Fête to collect a portion of it. And as for the boys, make 'em take a big share in running it—guiding people round the place, doing up parcels, running side-shows. Why not a display of some sort and a camp-fire sing-song to end up with ? "

" Not a bad idea, George ; I'll think it over."

" I should if I were you ; but don't forget to let the boys help in the thinking. Get a Court-of-Honour of your P.L.'s and make 'em work out some of the details. Why not get Aunt Emma on the job, too ? "

Bertie's face brightened considerably.

" Gad ! that's an idea," he said ; " and she'd just love it. I'll get her to come down at once and run the show."

" All right, Bertie ; but don't forget to let the boys run it too ; " and on this understanding we parted.

6

I felt afterwards that perhaps I had been over-hasty in suggesting the Garden Fête, and especially in mentioning Aunt Emma, otherwise the Dowager Countess of Middlewick, in connection with it.

I knew Bertie's Aunt Emma, and I might have foreseen that there would be little chance of anyone else getting a look-in if she really got interested in the show. And, of course, she did.

She was very fond of Bertie—she told me so on every possible occasion—and this fact, coupled with a capable and rather imperious nature, convinced her of the necessity for " seeing this thing through."

So the following week saw Emma Middlewick duly installed at the Tower House ; and one day she proposed herself to lunch with me, saying that she did so want to talk over dear Bertie's latest craze.

" I do think that it is *so* splendid of you, George, to get him to take up Boy Scouts," she said, as we sat down opposite one another at my little table. "You know that I think it will be *so* good for him."

We two were good friends, and therefore I had no hesitation in speaking my mind freely.

"I dare say it will be, *if* he sticks to it," I replied; "but what I am most concerned with is whether it will be so good for the boys. The fact of the matter is, dear lady, that I had nothing whatever to do with it. It was entirely Bertie's own idea, and I'm awaiting the result somewhat grimly. Scouting's not a thing to be treated as a passing craze."

"No, I suppose not," she replied rather vaguely. "I think the Boy Scouts are too splendid, George; and Bertie *will* do it so well."

"That remains to be seen," said I somewhat doubtfully. "It takes a lot of doing, Lady Middlewick. It's no earthly good if he's going off cruising in his yacht for half the summer, and going to shoot all the winter, and come back so tired that he doesn't want to do anything. That's just the trouble: Bertie's too impossibly rich."

Lady Middlewick sighed.

"I know. Poor, dear Bertie! But, if he sticks to it, it will be the making of him. Don't you think so, George?"

"A big 'if'," I replied, with a smile; and then added more hopefully: "But perhaps we shall pull it off between us. I can rely upon your help, anyhow, to keep him up to the mark."

"Of course, George. You know how anxious I am that he should have an aim in life. And now you *must* see the list of people who are going to help with the Fête."

And mercy! what a list it was! As far as I could see, the good lady had combed out the entire Peeress's Gallery in the House of Lords for the purpose.

I groaned inwardly and ventured to remark: "It's really splendid of you to take all this trouble, Lady

Middlewick. But where do the Scouts come in? You must make them feel that the show is partly theirs."

"Oh, that's all fixed, George," she replied brightly. "Bertie is full of ideas about that, and is quite decided that they shall do their bit. My beauty chorus from Mayfair, as you so rudely call them, are all coming down for the week; and, George, you must come and stay for it, too."

"Good Heavens, no! Spare me that," I gasped. "I should have to invest in a new tail-coat, and I'm a poor man."

"But you'll come to the Fête, at least?"

"Oh, yes, I'll come to the Fête, if only to see the boys doing their bit," I replied with a laugh; and we left it at that.

I've never seen such a Garden Fête as Bertie's, nor in all probability shall I again.

To start with, one could hardly move without cannoning into a Duchess or a Countess or at least some Dame of high degree. They were delightful people, but I got rather bored with a constant repetition of "*Dear* Bertie, isn't it splendid of him?" I felt like retorting, "Isn't it splendid of dear Bertie's money?" but refrained because I realised that such a remark would have been in doubtful taste and also not strictly true. For Bertie really excelled himself, and had been quite firm about the Scouts having a big share.

They had worked hard during the previous two months, passed their Tenderfoot Tests and duly taken the Promise (before myself at a special meeting arranged for the purpose), and now they were very much in evidence, running houp-la and clock-golf, tying up parcels, guiding people round the grounds, and making themselves generally useful. Also they put up a capital display of P.T. games, for which young Billingham had trained them, and finally gave a delightful camp-fire scene in a wooded corner of the garden. Bertie had a talent for stage management, and ran this part of the show himself, to the great delight of his loving relations and, in fact, of the whole large audience.

Of course, there were fireworks, a balloon race, tableaux and dancing, besides an array of well-furnished stalls.

Sir John was to have been the opener, but retired to bed with a chill the day before, and I took his place. I also took the opportunity of stressing the point about the importance of Scout Troops being self-supporting, and I saw Bertie grinning impudently at me while I was delivering my little speech. Afterwards he walked me round and made me buy all sorts of things I couldn't afford and didn't want, from chocolates to a jazz sweater. (The latter created something of a sensation at Parkwell later on ; it was so very jazz.)

But there can be no doubt about the success of the Fête : good weather, wonderful organisation, and crowds of people. It was overdone, of course ; would have been all right if it had been in aid of a fund for building a town hall or a cathedral, but was absurdly out of proportion for a Troop effort.

However, it had one excellent result, apart from the Wrexford Scouts. I forgot to say that Bertie had invited all the local Troops to come in free as his guests, entertained them to tea in the Riding School, and took particular trouble to get introduced to his brother-Scoutmasters, with the consequence that they all went away swearing by him. Later on he visited them in their own club-rooms, saying that he had come to pick their brains, and was extraordinarily nice to everyone.

The next step was his unanimous election to the Committee. Important, this, because in some way known only to Bertie it meant the subsequent disappearance of Scantling from our counsels. I don't know how he did it, and there are some things about which it is better not to inquire too closely. Bertie knew that I didn't like Scantling and couldn't get on with him, and, in fact, I had said that I would give something to get him moved on.

"Is that all your trouble ?" he asked innocently. "I think I can help you there. Just you leave it to me."

I didn't understand what he meant to do ; but, on the theory of grasping at any straw, I did leave it to him, and, as I say, Scantling sent in his resignation. I have never asked Bertie how it was done, and I have an idea that he would not have told me if I had. The main point is that we got a new Chairman in the person of old General Crawley, kindly and amenable, and the horizon in consequence looked brighter.

Late that summer both Bertie and I did a course at Parkwell. Needless to say, we enjoyed it mightily, in spite of somewhat depressing weather ; and I really believe that it was the one thing needed to confirm him in Scouting.

"What I like about this place," he confessed to me while we were out on the hike, "is that being a bloated plutocrat don't make a rap of difference—what ? I'm treated like a naughty little schoolboy. I should like to see Snadwell's face if we were to meet him round the next corner. And, George," he added, "I see exactly what you meant about not slobbering gold over the boys. You may kick me if you like—what ?"

And that is all I have to tell you about Bertie, except that the prophets were confounded, and that he found, as we have all found, that Scouting is a great game to be played with all one's might.

Nor have I anything further to say about Sledborough, beyond expressing a hope that I haven't made it appear that to me, and me alone, belongs the credit for the reign of peace and prosperity which followed these little incidents.

Rather let me give the credit for that to the players, diverse in thought and method as perhaps they were, and, above all, to the game itself.

VIII

THE WAR MEMORIAL

I

THOSE of you who are familiar with the great industrial city of Murchington will be inclined to agree that it is perhaps of all places upon the face of this earth the least salubrious and the most dispiriting.

Old Jim Strachey, Lieutenant-Colonel and District Commissioner of Boy Scouts, would tell you that it possesses but three redeeming features—the Oldroyd Park, the Union Club, and the 33rd Murchington Troop of his district. I should be inclined to add just one more, old Jim Strachey himself. He is, to my mind, a perfect example of the best type of English gentleman, and he is, moreover, my best friend.

When I first knew him, away back in 1911, he lived some twelve miles outside the reek of factory chimneys, and was as yet undisturbed by the gloom of the place, except when the wind set from the north-east.

From the first he had fallen a ready victim to the Scouting idea. At sixty years of age he had raised and become Scoutmaster of the 1st Danemow Troop, had taken a hand in the birth of the Murchington Association, had acted as its first Chairman, and was at the time of this episode District Commissioner for the South-East Division, the poorest and most thickly populated of an over-populated area.

It was he, indeed, who succeeded, with a persistence worthy of a better object, in persuading me to take a hand in the game. I want to be quite frank about myself. Somewhat lazy, very reluctant, and entirely taken up with doing nothing in particular, I had warned him that I loathed boys on principle, hated going out at nights, and should absolutely decline to make myself ridiculous in shorts. For some time I had maintained this attitude ; but Jim had persisted. He was good at persisting, in a quiet but exceedingly effective manner. He knew how to throw a fly over the sulky trout, did Jim, so that in the end the beast got caught without exactly knowing why or how.

He didn't stoop to flatter me ; didn't tell me that I should make a good Scoutmaster, or any nonsense of that sort ; but he talked about the little blighters with a quiet enthusiasm and a very genuine love, which was at least an earnest of his own sincerity.

And he was always amongst them, too, poking about in the most impossible slums ; never interfering, you know, but doing the big brother business in the most delightful manner possible.

Just to show you his methods, let me relate how he caught me, as he had caught many a better man before me.

I remember that he had asked me to accompany him to some show or other got up to interest the public. I remember it particularly because I had occasion to remind him that he had neglected to ask me to join up for at least two months.

"Oh, I'm not going to ask you again, Joe," Jim had replied ; "it's not everyone's job, and I'm not certain that it's yours. Anyhow, I am content to wait until you ask *me*."

My inexcusable pride at being able to do most things rather well, if I set my great mind to them, had felt piqued at this.

"Hang it all, Jim," I protested, "I commanded an M.I. Company for a whole year in S.A., and I believe that they were generally up to scratch."

"That's rather a different thing," he said. "There is a peculiar quality in the leadership of boys, especially slum boys, which is rare to come by. Look here, Joe, I'll take you down to see the 33rd to-night—one of the brightest oases in my desert. I'll introduce you to Mr. Geoffrey Kemble, a slim youth of twenty, who will show you in ten minutes exactly what I mean."

I thought for a moment. As a matter of fact, I had promised to make up a four for Bridge at the Club, and I dearly loved my Bridge. But, on the other hand, I could play any night of the week, and Jim had spoken so often, and with such quiet satisfaction, of this particular oasis of his that I had acquired a certain curiosity about the show.

"All right," I agreed. "I'll run you down in the car."

Jim demurred. "No, I don't think we'll use your plated Juggernaut on this trip. There is nowhere we can leave it, except in the open street, and someone might take a fancy to your lamps and gadgets. Come and have a scratch meal at 6.30, and we'll tram and foot it to Lower Capell Street."

I whistled softly. "Lower Capell Street? Isn't that where a beastly murder was committed two nights ago?" I asked.

"That's the jolly old spot," replied Jim—"at the house next door to the 33rd's headquarters. I'll show you things to-night, my boy. You shall see Scouting with a capital 'S.'"

And I'm bound to say that I did.

It was a bit of an eye-opener, was that visit. I had been gently reproved by Jim for using the word "inspection."

"We don't inspect, old man. We drop round and see some of the family."

Well, anyhow, "drop" wasn't a bad word to describe the process. We did drop—down into streets and alleys I didn't know existed; narrow and dirty and slushy, dark as the inside of a cow, tenanted by the denizens of a world which, I thanked God, was not mine. Slatternly women, expectorating men, squalling and inconceivably dirty babies of every shape and size. But Jim didn't seem to mind a bit.

"Behold the mothers and fathers, the little sisters and the little brothers of the gallant 33rd," said he. "And now for the Transformation Scene."

At that moment we turned into what I imagined was Lower Capell Street, for presently we came to a low door lit up by the rays of a hurricane-lamp held in the left hand of a small Boy Scout. With the remaining hand he saluted. Jim grasped his left hand, as soon as the lamp could be deposited for the purpose, and inquired: "Hullo, Dickie! that you? Mr. Kemble inside?"

"Not come yet, sir," quoth the urchin. "Should be here soon, though; I'm waiting for him."

"All right, we'll go through. Mind the steps, Joe! It's mortal dark."

We picked our way carefully down the so-called steps, along a passage and up to a door, behind which were unmistakable signs of the presence of boy in the lump.

"The curtain goes up," said Jim, as he rapped in a peculiar manner. "They have evolved a code," he explained, "for the purpose of avoiding raids on the part of unbelievers in the neighbourhood."

At the signal pandemonium ceased, the bolts were withdrawn, and I got my first sight of young Kemble's crew.

I suppose that there were some thirty boys present, all but two or three of whom were in uniform, and ranging in age from twelve to seventeen or so.

I am bound to admit that I was impressed both by their appearance and by their captivating manners, for they all saluted us quite nicely and grinned "Good evening." I noticed that each boy held some sort of a pole or bludgeon in one hand, and that a small football was trying to make up its mind where to settle in the middle of the floor.

"Good evening, all," said Jim. "Playing 'Crash 'em'? Good! Mr. Gage will play for one side, and I'll take t'other. Come on, Joe."

A pole was thrust into my hand.

"You take my place, sir," invited an obliging Scout. "I've took it on the shin. Don't think it's broke, though," he added as an afterthought.

Anyhow, there was I, nicely fitting clothes (I pride myself on my clothes), spats and all, wielding a pole and trying to hit a very elusive ball with the butt thereof, while Jim danced and shouted encouragement at the other end of the room.

Apparently there were no rules. You just tried to hit that ball, anyhow and anywhere. If you failed you almost certainly hit someone else's shins. Mine were rapped extremely hard about four times, and once I measured my length on the floor. It was during the slight breathing space allowed me, while I was being pulled to my feet and politely dusted down, that I appealed to Jim on this point.

"Rules?" said he. "There are neither rules nor goals in this game. We probably shouldn't keep the first nor find the second if there were, so we prefer to do without. Come on, play!" And there we were at it again.

I cannot pretend that I was particularly sorry when the door opened once more and disclosed Dickie of the lamp, closely followed by one whom I took to be Scoutmaster Geoffrey Kemble.

2

I am bound to say that my first impression of the sheikh of Jim's oasis was one of slight disappointment. I don't quite know what manner of man I had expected —certainly not a stalwart capable of tackling any two of his bigger boys single-handed, nor even an immaculate young gentleman bringing the freshness of daily baths into a region where such things are practically unknown.

It was, I think, his extreme youth which surprised me most. He did not look his twenty years ; and as to his slimness, one might have described him as a reed to be shaken by the lightest of breezes. It was not, indeed, until he had greeted me with a smile which lit up his whole face that I was enabled to see behind the disadvantages of a poor physique and recognise some of the personality and charm which I got to know and appreciate so well later on.

Jim's introduction was typical.

" Geoff, here's some fertile ground. Let's call it Joe Gage's plot. Sow your seed, like a good fellow."

Kemble smiled again—smiling appeared to be a habit of his—as he replied : " I hope we shan't bore you, sir. We are going to have just an ordinary Troop night, you know—nothing very wonderful."

I assured him that, from what I had already seen of the ordinary Troop nights of the 33rd, boredom wasn't likely to worry me.

" I don't think, though," I added, " that I'll take part in another game of ' Crash 'em ' until I've bought a pair of shin-pads."

" There will be no need for that, Mr. Gage," said Kemble. " We blow off steam first and then settle down to business. Shall I carry on, Colonel ? "

Jim nodded, and hauled me off to the other side of the room, where we perched ourselves precariously on a pair of parallel-bars like two hens on a roosting-perch. " Crash 'em " was resumed in a minor key, while Kemble conferred with the biggest boy present, a great hulking lad who sported three white stripes on his left breast and who, I was told, went by the rank and name of Troop-Leader Dale.

Presently a whistle sounded, pandemonium died down, the dilapidated ball was neatly dribbled under our perch, and the words " Patrol Corners " sent the boys in four equal groups into each corner of the room.

" Leaders, call the roll and collect subscriptions," was the next order—but perhaps " order " is hardly the word, it was so quietly spoken. I was to learn that everything about Geoffrey Kemble was quiet, but none the less efficient and to the point.

During the subdued haggling which ensued I looked about me and took stock of the room, and, with Jim's aid, learnt something of its history.

" Used to be an old school, and was going to be pulled down until we saved it." The " we " I took to be Jim himself. " Each Patrol has its own corner," he went on, " and they are responsible that everything in that corner is kept shipshape."

At one end was a large copy of " The Scout Law," and underneath a bit of board bearing the words " This Week's Law," with one of them—something about being kind to animals—affixed thereto. I inquired the meaning of this.

" Oh, that," Jim informed me, " is one of Geoff's ways of keeping the young beggars up to scratch. If he notices anything going wrong he just sticks up the Scout Law in question for a week, and leaves them guessing what the trouble is. On Saturday night he tells them—without mentioning names—and the guilty one gets a quiet talk in private. Rather ingenious—and it works. And mind you," he added, " it wouldn't work if that boy didn't live as nearly as possible up to that sheet of type himself."

Another thing I inquired about was the fact that the boys all subscribed to the show, and yet I imagined that they must be as poor as Lucifer.

" Of course they subscribe." said Jim. " They run this little game themselves, and they help to pay for its running. All their kit was paid for by the boys themselves, helped by occasional whist-drives and dances which they give in this room. In spite of their poverty, they're mighty proud, Joe; make no mistake about that."

This set me thinking hard; and there were many interesting items still unexplained when the whistle went again, and brought the Patrols doubling to the centre of the room till they were formed up like the spokes of a wheel, with Kemble and Dale as the hub.

The words "Alert! Salute!" were given, a cord was jerked, and a small Union Jack broken out from the ceiling.

"At ease!" said Kemble. "Will you come round, Colonel, with Mr. Gage?"

It was this cursory inspection of the boys which impressed me perhaps as much as anything I had yet seen of them. To begin with, they knew how to stand straight and still, and they were clean—clean in every detail of uniform and equipment. Jerseys, stockings and shorts were darned and patched all over, it is true, but they showed the signs of much hard usage combined with a proper pride in the wearing.

After the conclusion of this little ceremony Kemble issued various instructions to his Patrol Leaders, from which it would appear that the Woodpeckers were to revise the Tenderfoot Tests (whatever those might be), the Owls would dip into the mysteries of Campcraft, the Eagles were to learn how to recognise various trees and what they were used for, while the Otters were given the task of constructing a trestle out of spars and sundry bits of rope. And this is where I got another mild shock. The instruction of each Patrol was undertaken by the Patrol Leaders themselves, while Kemble wandered from group to group doing nothing.

I expressed my astonishment to Jim, who merely grunted, "That's leadership. Geoff trains his P.L.'s, and trusts them to carry on. Doesn't butt in unless anything goes wrong. But it means work, Joe, my lad—much work behind the scenes. You'll find it no sinecure if you intend to do the job properly."

Jim appeared to have taken it for granted that I was so intending, but I let it pass at the moment, as my attention was engaged elsewhere. The Patrol Leaders held the boards for twenty minutes ; then the whole Troop took part in a series of intricate and wonderful games, which were explained to me by Kemble as a more amusing form of physical training than jerks and dumb-bells.

After ten minutes of this, they assembled once more round their Scoutmaster, who announced as follows: " Starmanship Class under myself in the den ; fall out, those working for Starman. Tenderfoot Scouts under the Troop-Leader in the Woodpeckers' corner—special Campcraft instruction." Then he looked at me and calmly continued : " The Master-at-Arms Class under Mr. Gage at the far end."

All eyes were turned to me as I appealed to Jim.

" No good, Joe," said the old wretch. " I told them that you got your Blue and won the Army Officers' Middleweights ; so you're for it, me lad."

And I was. And what is more, I enjoyed myself mightily teaching those youngsters. They were so desperately keen, and two at least had quite an idea of the game, enough to keep me busy and make me very hot. I hadn't boxed for years, and felt my lack of training by the time we had all had enough. Also, my personal appearance had altered since I had first entered the room—" for the better," Jim was unkind enough to remark.

But I was beginning to think that he was right, and that possibly I had been living for some considerable time under a strange delusion.

I need not chronicle the remainder of that evening in detail. Such as it was it must be familiar to many who read these words. There was, I remember, a wonderful camp-fire made from an electric torch and red paper, with the rest of the room in darkness. We all gathered round, and sang choruses and told yarns ; and, as the red glow fell upon that circle of eager faces, I thought of Jim's remark about the fathers and mothers of the gallant 33rd. And then there were a few prayers, the flag was saluted as it gently fluttered from the ceiling, and presently we found ourselves outside again in the murk of Lower Capell Street.

I turned to my mentor of the evening.

" How is it all done ? " I asked.

Jim laid his hand on my shoulder, and gave me a gentle shove as he replied : " That's just what I want you to go and find out."

3

Three months later I applied to Jim for a Scoutmaster's warrant. Much of the intervening time had been spent in regular visits to the 33rd, including a memorable week in camp.

It was, in fact, that week on Brydale Moor which finally decided me—seven sunny days, which gave me a deeper insight into the game of Scouting than all the rest of my probation put together.

I admit that Jim had had a great deal to do with rousing me from my lethargy of idleness ; Kemble, with his singleness of purpose and simple faith, had more. But it was the boys themselves who had tugged the hardest.

A merry crowd were the 33rd, following a leader cheerfully and whole-heartedly because their young instinct told them that it was good so to do. And when we raced across the Moor to the brook which they had dammed up into a bathing-pool, or gathered round the glowing logs for our evening sing-song, I found myself thinking of Lower Capell Street and thanking God for the game of Scouting.

Jim accepted my decision as a matter of course. He had angled for me with commendable patience—why, Heaven knows—and had landed me with tact and skill. But he displayed no great triumph in the result ; merely told me that I was deuced lucky to be able to start life afresh, and thereafter appointed me to the task—no light one—of reviving the past glories of the 35th.

I need not enter into the details of that most hectic period of my existence, with all its hopes, fears, and petty disappointments ; nor need I recount at length my wordy warfare with the local incumbent, which ended (as far as I can recollect) all square ; nor even the exasperating way in which three successive clubrooms were sold over our heads, until we finally settled down in Meads Lane.

Many a budding Scoutmaster has gone through what I went through, and worse, but not many have had a Jim Strachey or a Kemble to whom they could turn when exasperation or apparent lack of all result threatened to swamp early enthusiasm. My deepest woes floated away like so many bubbles before the breath of Jim's stout optimism, to burst and disappear into thin air after a visit to Lower Capell Street.

It was these occasional evenings spent with the 33rd which proved to me beyond argument what I was at first slow to perceive, that it was rarely the boy, never the game, and almost invariably myself that was at fault when troubles came.

And so I stuck it out, and grew in wisdom and knowledge of it—and loved it—until the War came, and took us from our camps and from our boys, and hurled us out like so many atoms into the void.

Geoff and I, of course, went almost at once, he to his Territorial Battalion and I to a commission in the county Yeomanry Regiment, which I obtained through Jim's good offices.

He, dear old boy, too old to fight and hating himself for it, spent his days in the organisation and recruiting of "K" Armies and his evenings in the nursing of his leaderless Scout Troops. And so the most of them survived throughout those long, weary, wonderful years.

Jim was a good correspondent, and kept me supplied

with news, which reached me in the most out-of-the-way places. Thus I heard of Geoff's wound and accompanying M.C. when I was in the flooded trenches at Suvla Bay, and of his being invalided out badly gassed while I was climbing the rugged mountains east of Jordan.

I heard only once from Geoff himself, and that was to tell me of Jimmy Baynes's death. I remembered Jimmy as Patrol Leader of the Eagles, full of life and keen as mustard on his Troop and on everything connected with Scouting. He had been drafted to Geoff's Battalion, and had shown particular aptitude for sniping until, alas! he fell a victim to one of that unpleasant fraternity on the other side of No-man's Land.

Geoff didn't say much, only told me the bare facts; but I knew what he would feel about the boy whom he had taken into the 33rd straight from a Juvenile Court and who had responded so readily to his influence and leadership.

After it was all over I stayed on in the Near East on one job or another until the early months of 1920. The life suited me, and I liked the country. I think also that, like many another, I rather dreaded getting back to an existence which must henceforth be passed in the absence of many an old friend and contemporary.

It is quite possible that I should have stayed out there considerably longer if Jim had not been so persistent in his efforts to get me back.

"There is plenty to do at home," he wrote; "more than ever there was. I'm getting old, Joe, and I want you to help me with the boys; they are the most important people nowadays. And I'm not quite happy about Geoff."

It was this last sentence, coupled with my third attack of malaria, which finally decided me to pack up the old valise and shake the sand of the desert from off my feet.

I went down to Murchington two days after I landed,

and found Jim looking older, but otherwise much the same. The old boy looked me up and down.

"In spite of your malaria," he said, "it's done you good—thinned you down a bit."

"Oh, I'm fit enough now," I replied, "but I don't want to talk about myself—at least, not yet. Tell me about the boys—and about Geoff."

Jim's face clouded over. "The boys are all right," he said; "Geoff has been looking after your lot as well as his own since he came back. We knocked 'em down to two Patrols apiece; and there were times, Joe, when I found them just about thirty too many as it was. But we managed to keep going somehow—only lost two Troops in the whole district—until Geoff came home. He started work again—but it's not quite the same Geoff somehow. He was badly gassed, you know, and sometimes gets fits of depression lasting for days at a time. He's come into money, too—bought a car and taken to golf. Not that I mind that; but he has cut his Scout evenings down to one a week, and the other night I hear he lost his temper and sacked one of his P.L.'s. I've never known him do a thing like that before.

"He's had one or two bad disappointments with the boys, I know. The young beggars are more difficult than ever now. But five years ago his love of the game, and gift for it, would have pulled him through all that. The charm is there still, and, I believe, the gift, but I'm doubtful about the enthusiasm—what you call the vital spark, Joe. The boy is a bit unbalanced; had the impudence to tell me the other day that he thought of chucking the whole thing. I told him that I thought he was making a mistake. I wish you'd go round and do the same."

I had to return to London for a Medical Board that evening, but I promised to do what I could as soon as I was free.

I couldn't believe in the possibility of Geoff chucking Scouting. I preferred to treat the trouble as a passing phase brought about by the shock of what he had gone through to a highly strung system. It was inconceivable to me that he could really be contemplating giving up the whole show. The bare idea left a blank feeling in my mind. But I knew that the War had left more than bodily scars on many natures such as his—I had heard of cases something like it before—and I hoped to heaven, as I walked down the street to his house, that if ever I had possessed any influence over him it would come to my aid now.

I rehearsed more than one line of argument during that short walk; but I was certainly not prepared to find him as I did, sunk deep in a chair and reading *Scouting for Boys*.

We hadn't seen each other since those fateful days of 1914, and our greetings were suitable to the occasion. These preliminaries over, he looked across at me with a smile and remarked:

"You've seen the Colonel, of course, and he sent you round to talk to me like a father—isn't that about it, Joe?"

"You're near the mark, Geoff, old son," I replied, "but I'm not going to call you anything until I've heard all about the trouble."

He turned the leaves of his book idly for a moment, and then looked up again.

"Joe, I don't know what the Colonel told you about me, but he was quite right. A week ago I was everything you like to call me, but "—he held up *Scouting for Boys*—"I think I see daylight now."

I could plainly see that the youngster was troubled in mind and wanted to talk, but I didn't wish to force his confidence.

Presently he turned to me suddenly with rather a wan smile and asked: "Would it bore you, Joe, if I told you all about it?"

I sank deeper into my chair and began to fill a pipe.

"My dear boy," I said, "it will bore me just about as

much as my first night with the 33rd. Go on; spout it out."

Geoff's face grew a shade brighter. "Thanks, Joe," he said; "you have the gift of understanding." He paused for a moment as if at a loss for words, and then continued: "You know that I got rather badly messed up, though God knows I've got no right to complain. Nobody who came back whole from that has a right to grouse. But I get these fits—doctor says it's the result of gas—when nothing seems right, when I only want to be left alone to nurse my own worries, when even Scouting, Joe, seems a tiresome drudgery, leading nowhere.

"I lost my temper once—I expect the Colonel told you—and sacked my best P.L. He came back, of course; but that's not the point. Then the doctor told me to try golf, and I did, and got keener on it than on the Troop. I started arriving late at meetings, and then I cut them down to one a week. I *am* a brute, Joe; I wouldn't take them to camp at Whitsun because I wanted to play in some wretched competition, and your boys were being neglected just the same.

"At last I couldn't stick it any longer, and told the Colonel that I was going to chuck Scouting altogether. And what do you think he did? Didn't curse me; didn't even say he was sorry to hear it. He just said: 'All right, Geoff; but I don't think you are giving yourself a fair chance. If you've quite made up your mind, there is nothing more to be said, and perhaps a rest will do you good.' And just as I was leaving the room, feeling every kind of a beast, he called me back and reminded me that the Memorial was going to be unveiled the following Saturday, and asked me to bring the boys along for the last time. Said that he had been invited to do the unveiling, and that he'd feel lost without the 33rd.

"Not a word of reproach, Joe—only a request to have the Troop that he'd nursed all through the War for me there to help him. You can imagine what I felt like when I gave him my promise."

I nodded. "I think I can," I said. "But go on; I'm getting interested."

"Well," he continued, "I'd already told the Troop that I wasn't going on, and we'd started dismantling the room. But I got them together for the Saturday afternoon—they turned out as smart as paint, Joe, though, as far as they knew, it was to be their last show—and we duly turned up at the church. Everyone was there, of course—the Colonel and the Bishop, who did the dedication; and old Briskett, who made a fortune out of bad blankets and was trying to look sorrowful about it; and Lane the publican, who made all that trouble about billeting; and Jackson of the sugar scandal. By God, Joe! when one thinks of the men out there, what they did and what they suffered, it's an offence against decency that such should be allowed to be present. And then, after the Colonel had pulled the cord and released the Union Jack, he spoke. Quite short and simple it was, but I shall never forget his last few words."

The boy took a cutting from the table and went on: "This is what he said, Joe: 'It is fitting that we, parishioners of St. Michael's, should have raised up this beautiful Cross of Sacrifice as an outward and visible sign that we shall ever honour the memory of those who gave their all. But it is not enough; they will expect more of us who are left than mere wood and stone. There is a civilisation to be rebuilt, and each one of us, in his or her own sphere, can help in the rebuilding.

"'The need for personal sacrifice did not end with the signing of the Armistice. In the coming years it may even be that we shall be called upon to prove that, just as they gave their all, so are we ready to give and to do what we can to help the common weal.

"'As I go about to-day I see around me a growing need for social service of all kinds. To some of us the gift for this has been given. It is surely in the proper use of all such gifts, God-given as they are, that we can best keep faith with our dead.'

"Joe, I felt that he was speaking to me when he spoke those words, and I saw myself just about on a level with Briskett and Co. After it was all over we marched back to the clubroom, and the boys asked whether they should finish taking the pictures down. They even seemed keen to do it, as if to show that at any rate they were going to do their part, whatever it cost. And they tried to be cheerful about it, but some of them were looking pretty cheap, poor youngsters! And then I found that there were only three pictures left up, and they were the photographs of Jimmy Baynes and the two Rowleys, our own little War Memorial.

"Joe, I simply couldn't tell them to take those down. I just told them all to clear out for five minutes. And when they were gone, I thought about how those three had loved the Troop, especially Jimmy. Do you remember how keen he was, Joe? I stood looking at his photograph, and it seemed almost as if his eyes reproached me—as well they might.

"There was only one thing I could do. I called the boys back, and asked them if they'd like to put all the pictures back again, because the Troop was going on, only better than it had ever been before. And then came the hardest part of all, Joe, for they cheered me as if they were never going to stop. And I felt all the time that it was the Colonel and those three who deserved their cheers, not my miserable self. And I haven't had the face to tell him yet."

I rose, knocked out my pipe, and pulled him from his chair.

"We'll go together, Geoff, old son," I said, "and tell him that between us we are going to make Scouting just about hum down here."

IX

ONE SUMMER'S DAY

THIS is a tale about camp—just an ordinary day in a Scout camp.

And yet I wonder whether I have started it as happily as I might. I somehow think that perhaps I haven't used quite the right words; for it is not exactly a tale, and no day like this at Ripley Pool can ever be ordinary.

Let me rather call it a sketch—a memory if you will—something which, along with its fellows, lives with us down the years, and never fails to soothe and satisfy.

The scene may have changed, the actors therein have dispersed, but both will come back readily to the mind, the one standing out against the other, fresh with life and happiness as if it were but yesterday.

Scenes of other and different camps may crowd the background—camps with long lines of well-dressed tents bespattered with the mud of parallel walks between, and where the presiding genii were a Colonel, an Adjutant and a Battalion Sergeant-Major.

Unromantic people, these; but who could blame them? There is little of romance in mud and army discipline, in fallings-in and fallings-out, in strident bugle-calls and the constant rattle of accoutrements.

Not even the memory of those nights when we stole away in the wet and cold for an unknown destination can stir us now to aught but a faint shudder. It was a grim and serious business.

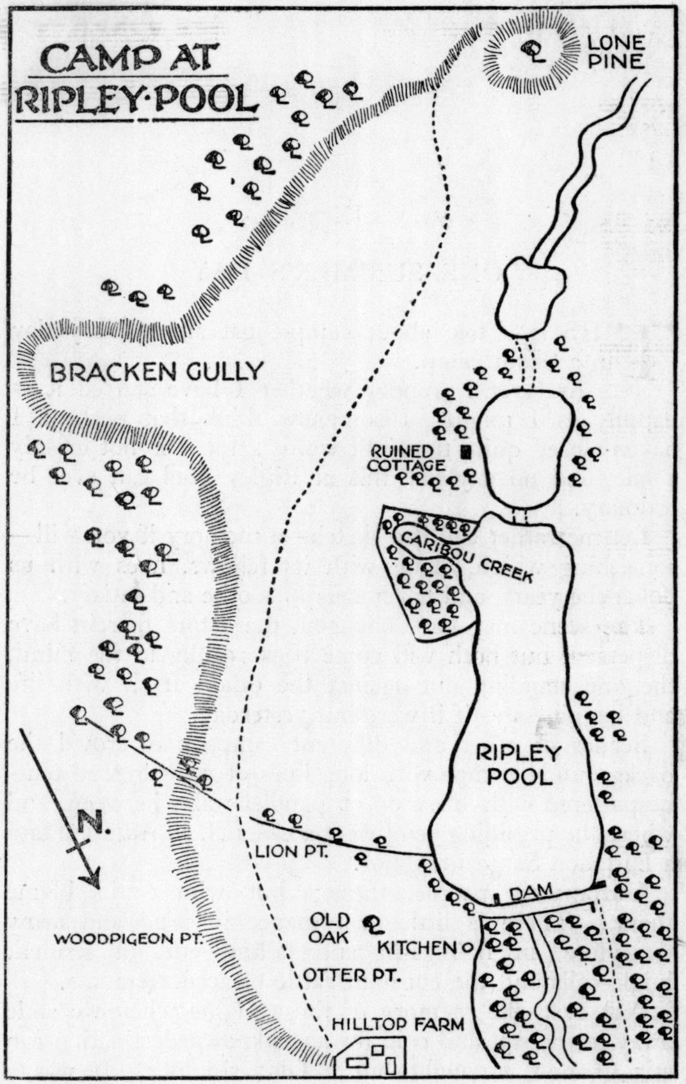
CAMP AT
RIPLEY·POOL
LONE
PINE
BRACKEN GULLY
RUINED
COTTAGE
CARIBOU CREEK
RIPLEY
POOL
N.
LION PT.
DAM
OLD
OAK
KITCHEN
WOODPIGEON PT.
OTTER PT.
HILLTOP FARM

There is, of course, a serious side to our Scout camps also, but it is a seriousness clothed in romance, a purpose cloaked in freedom, a great game in a gay setting. For the setting, if not everything, is important: the smooth green turf, the trees, the distant hills away beyond the lake, the bracken. It is in the perfect setting that we most readily capture the spirit of the bold pioneer, the kindness of Nature, and the freedom of simple things.

There is a valley, which I know and love, set deep in its wooded hills, where the Scouts are wont to pitch their tents.

They have chosen well, for there can be few places in old England better adapted to their game than this valley.

Unkempt and uncared for, no forester's axe trims its covers nor thins out the giant forest trees.

The little stream which feeds the many pools can be heard but seldom seen, because of a tangle of undergrowth which meets overhead. Even the dams which brought the pools into being, and still sustain their mighty weight of water, are hidden beneath a half-century's growth of bullrushes and meadow plants.

The largest pool of all, some thirty acres in extent, starts modestly at its upper end under a coverlet of reeds and water-lilies, where wildfowl breed and the grey herons fish. But it broadens gradually to thrust its full weight against the great dam at the lower end—broadens and deepens. The reeds hug the bank here; the lilies also, for they cannot reach down their rope-like stems through thirty feet of water.

At one end of this dam is an old red-brick boat-house half-hidden in foliage; at the other a battered gate gives on to a smooth, gently sloping expanse of turf fringed with bracken and shaded by an ancient oak—a King Charles's oak, so they say. Personally I doubt the legend, for if the unhappy monarch climbed all the oaks which bear his name hereabouts, he must have spent a goodly portion of his days up a tree.

Be that as it may, it is a gnarled and gallant old giant, and one of value, too. Whether or no a King of England honoured its branches with his royal person, at least the flag of old England can be seen fluttering gaily from the most withered of them on many a summer's day.

It is the centre of camp, this old tree—the common meeting place where Lions, Woodpigeons and Otters assemble at their Scoutmaster's whistle.

Some distance off, and widely scattered, lie their own little camps, in front of which the Patrol flags are fluttering; and one of these, we note, is adorned with the red and yellow ribbons of the Lions, for they were adjudged to have the cleanest pitch that morning.

Down by the gate, under a wide-spreading beech, whose healthy branches form a shelter impervious to rain, is the kitchen, with its pots and pans, dishcloths and wipers hanging on the fence near by. There are some log seats, a rough table, and four rabbits hanging on a branch, to complete this part of the picture.

The camp appears to be almost empty. Only a few boys are to be seen, and these are grouped round the table and fire preparing dinner, while watching them from the door of his tent some twenty yards away is one whom we take to be the Scoutmaster.

He is smoking a pipe and cleaning his boots, for apparently he has nothing to do for the moment but to smoke his pipe and clean his boots; and the morning is in itself something of a reaction.

After two depressing days of ceaseless rain the Troop had turned out at seven o'clock with the sun already hot on the tents and a cloudless sky holding the promise of a dry day.

Good swimmers had been able to test the strength of the little landing-stage, to the building of which much thought had been given.

He and four of the biggest of them had used the stage as diving-board and ladder, and though it had rocked and creaked under the strain, they had noted with great satisfaction that there had been no sinking of the trestles nor movement of the deep-driven bollards.

There was some cause for satisfaction in this, because, although they had often launched such a trestle from the top of the sunk fence near Troop Headquarters, this had been their first attempt to build anything for strenuous service over real water ; and his Scouts would now realise the value of tight, accurate lashings and measurements.

And so there had been something of wonder and much of self-congratulation at the strength of the little structure when the burly Leader of the Woodpigeons had taken the first bold plunge from the end of the stage that morning.

The Scoutmaster smiled when he remembered the boys' pride in an achievement born of his own instruction. The smile became a chuckle as he recalled to mind the look of consternation on the face of Tenderfoot James Spence as that same Patrol Leader, on coming to the surface after a second dive, had spotted him and shouted : " Hi ! look at Jimmy Spence washing with all his clothes on. Get hold of him, Jack. That's right, taken 'em off him." And poor Jimmy had been forcibly relieved of two shirts and a vest and his back and head splashed with cold water. And yet but five years had elapsed since the author of his tribulation had gone through much the same operation.

What a useful thing Troop tradition was ! the Scoutmaster thought, as he put the clean boots inside his tent and strolled down to the lakeside. And what a day it was, too ! The blankets sprawling over every bush were being aired by the hot sun just as they should be aired, the lightest of cool breezes stirred the surface of the water into tiny ripples, and a slight mist scarcely veiled the blue-green of Whinberry Hill away to the west.

As he walked along the dam to the old boat-house three distinct and pleasant sounds came to him from varying distances.

Away at the top of the lake, by Caribou Creek (there were no caribou, nor was it exactly a creek—but what matter ?), the tap-tap of an axe and an occasional crack indicated the Otters at work on the wood-supply. Nearer at hand the cooking operations were being directed by Joe Pedley, Leader of the Woodpigeons. Joe himself was making a roly-poly pudding, but it seems that he had time to think of the first course while he plied his rolling-pin on the second.

"Now then, Tom, finished skinning them rabbits ? Only three, mind; I want the other to bake in clay, and three's enough for the stew. All right, put 'em in, and don't forget the salt. Stop making a mess with that axe, Jack, and lend a hand. Put some more wood on the fire and shove on that pot. Not too much, or you'll put the blessed thing out, man. Where have you been, Jim ? Well, you should have done that afore. Lend a hand with the spuds ; no, get me the jam first—black currant if there is any ; it's in the big box at the back of the store-tent. Here come the Lions with the water at last. 'Bout time, too—lazy blighters. Hi ! hurry up, you chaps ; we want that."

This last in a stentorian shout, which had not the least quickening effect. The Lions had some excuse. It is difficult, not to say rash, to hurry unduly when carrying buckets of water slung on Scout staves down a steep bank. It is so much safer and pleasanter to proceed slowly to the tune of "London's burning," especially when you come to the line which states "Go fetch me some water."

In addition to water, milk, butter, eggs and a kindly welcome were all obtainable at Hilltop Farm, scarce two hundred yards from the camp, but quite hidden by the rising ground. Letters and the newspapers were also left there by arrangement with the local postman, and it was one of the duties of the milk and water Patrol to bring these back to camp with them.

The Scoutmaster went up the hill to meet them and to help Nobby, who was struggling along manfully under the weight of two buckets of water almost as big as himself.

"Got any letters, Sam?" he asked the Leader. "Thanks. When you've hung the milk-can in the pool, just run along the bank and shout to the Otters to come in, or they'll demolish the whole coppice."

Sam went off at a trot, and presently the third Patrol came into view round the corner of the wood by Caribou Creek harnessed dog-team fashion to the laden trek-cart.

Their progress was not swift, for the load was heavy, the ground rough, and they were, besides, too much taken up with facetious conversation and its resultant merriment to pull well as a team.

But at last they creaked and rolled and laughed their way into camp, and set to work stacking the wood in its allotted space, handy to the fire.

"Good man, Arthur!" said the Scoutmaster. "Mostly walnut and apple, isn't it? Do fine for camp-fire to-night. Most of the villagers are coming down, I believe, so we shall want a good blaze.

"Put the axes safe and hang the rope on the fence there, and then get the Otters together again; we are going to fall in in two ticks. Joe, leave someone to look after dinner—Geoff will do; he's got a stiff knee—and get your lot together, too. Lions, finished stacking that wood? Righto!" And the whistle went.

Immediately there ensued a wild race for the oak, and in an incredibly short time the Patrols were formed up on three sides of a square facing its mighty bole.

The Otters were adjudged winners of the little race, but lost two of the resulting good marks because Alec would insist on chattering.

The Scoutmaster's rule was light; but one thing he did insist upon, and that was absolute silence when the Troop had fallen in. Usually he got it, but sometimes there were lapses, and marks dropped in the Inter-Patrol Competition. Moreover, he had found out, after a long and varied experience of Scout camps, that it paid to work his boys hard all the morning and get the essential things done before dinner-time.

To-day half an hour was to be given to Patrol instruction.

So let us climb in spirit to King Charles's precarious seat in the old tree and listen to what he has to say.

"Your jobs seem to have been done well this morning," he began, "though we shall know more what the Pigeons have been up to after we have eaten their dinner. But you were a bit slow getting that wood, Otters. We marked those trees yesterday, so that you could go straight to them, and it hasn't left us much time.

"But still there's enough for half an hour's Patrol work under the Seconds. I want each of you Leaders to do me a rapid sketch-map of Glazon Bridge, taking in all ground within a hundred yards. Your note-books will do; suit the scale to them, and be back here by 12.15. Now for the rest. Lions, your axemanship wasn't very good yesterday. Ken, run through the main points with them, and split a few logs.

"Woodpigeons, I want you to establish two Semaphore Stations, one here and t'other at the top of Bracken Gully. Jack, I'll give you a message to transmit, and the far station can come in when they have sent the answer.

"Otters, you have had the hard job this morning. You can judge some distances and tree heights. Bob, I'll let you have a key plan for them, and give you the correct answers when they have all done. Now, half an hour only, mind; then bathing. Alert! Break away!"

The boys went off with their Seconds and the Scoutmaster to his tent to get the promised directions, and for a time all was peace again—comparative peace, for wherever there be Scouts in camp there will be happy chatter and sparkling wit from Rouse-out till Lights-out, and even past that somewhat uncertain hour.

It is unnecessary to relate the details of the half-hour's instruction which followed, but we may note that the Seconds appear to be quite capable of keeping their charges in reasonable subjection and of imparting a certain amount of fascinating knowledge.

For the Scoutmaster had always reckoned his Seconds as the spare wheel of the concern. From the first he had been determined to do as little detail work himself as possible, and to rely upon his Leaders to run their own little shows.

But he had discovered, in the very early days of the Troop, that a country Scoutmaster cannot always count upon his Leaders turning up to time, owing to pressure of work on farm or railway, and so his Seconds were trained to take their places if need arose.

On this occasion he wandered round, but did not interfere. Some details of the teaching might have been given more accurately or with better point, but he had always made it a rule to talk the matter over with the instructor afterwards, and not in the presence of the instructed.

Presently he again blew his whistle, long and loud, and shouted the magic word "Bathing"; and soon the camp was alive with boys in the very scantiest of clothing, for the day was hot and the water near at hand.

The three Leaders, who had returned and given in their rough sketch-maps—two of them very rough and the third neat but rather inaccurate—went down to the lakeside, unloosed the chain of an ancient but trustworthy punt, and got aboard with the safe swimmers, giants at the sport, who could fool about in thirty feet of water as though it was a hip-bath.

The remainder repaired to the shade of a great beech overhanging a favourite spot, where the bottom remained at a reasonable distance for some ten yards out from the bank. Where it deepened suddenly and tactlessly the boys had planted a semicircle of stakes driven down into the mud, and within this space there was soon much merriment and a mighty splashing—also occasionally a spasmodic effort to swim, were it only three or four convulsive strokes, helped and guided by the Scoutmaster himself.

Nobby showed perhaps the greatest persistence—so much so that he convinced himself, if no one else, that he was now ready to pass his ten yards' test, success in which meant ten marks to the Lions.

But Nobby had over-estimated his skill, a thing which he was apt to do, and had covered but half the distance with a great commotion of arms and legs before he collided with the bank, and scraped his chest on a fresh-water mussel—a gallant effort with a sad ending.

So let us pass on to the next incident—dinner. In camp breakfast is delightful, if the morning be fine and the porridge unburnt, especially if it follows close upon an early morning bathe.

How fragrant and satisfying is the tea out of an enamelled tin mug! How delicious the sizzling bacon and the eggs fresh from Hilltop Farm!

Can anything match a frying-pan full of newly-gathered mushrooms or the thin slice of bread fried in bacon fat?

No *chef* of Ritz or Carlton can compete with such a meal as this. For the dew is on the grass, the early sun has turned the lake to a sheet of blue and silver set in emerald, and the blue wood-smoke hangs in a fragrant mist about the tree-tops.

But dinner! Isn't there something even more wonderful about dinner? If breakfast is a pleasant necessity, dinner is a solemn rite. It is far more than the mere satisfying of a ravenous appetite, for into its preparation has gone much thought, necessitated by the possibility of rude criticism on the part of those who didn't cook but have to eat it.

As Geoff remarked, any ass can cook porridge or eggs and bacon, but it takes a cook to prepare and nurse a stew which shall be above reproach.

Exciting things are camp stews ; like a lucky dip, you never know what your portion may contain. Every boy had brought with him some home-grown offering to swell the common larder. There were carrots, turnips, onions, parsnips, and goodness knows what else to reinforce the spuds, the meat scraps and the rabbits.

" Smells good," said Nobby, as he peered into the seething mess, the incident of the fresh-water mussel quite forgotten.

" Of course it smells good," rejoined Joe. " I tell you the Woodpigeons made it, and they know how to do these things. They don't burn 'em like the Otters, *nor* forget the salt like the Lions. Come along, up with your plates. Now then, get in line there, and wait your turn."

And after the stew the roly-poly pudding, which actually hadn't burst its bag and let all the jam boil away. And finally a few words from the Scoutmaster.

" Jolly good dinner ! I propose a vote of thanks to the Woodpigeons, especially to their Patrol Leader who conceived it, and to Geoff who nursed it through its later stages. Carried unanimously.

" Now, which is the washing-up Patrol. Lions ? Well, get to work, and then all rest till two o'clock, at which hour the Otters will attempt to get a dispatch through to Lone Pine while the remainder do their best to prevent them.

" R.E.S.T., please, which, being interpreted, means sitting or lying about in the shade, reading or writing home to mother. Slumber is permitted—indeed, advised—but skylarking is taboo.

"Leaders, come to my tent for a few minutes, just to get the idea of the thing. You can then work out the plan of attack and defence with your Patrols while they are resting."

It was a very exciting game—not that it differed much probably from all games of a like kind.

Two Patrols occupied a line from Caribou Creek to Bracken Gully. They concealed themselves amongst the bracken and furze-bushes, trying hard not to talk for twenty minutes, while the Otters used every wile known to Scouting to get through to Lone Pine, at which spot the Troop Leader was posted to receive them.

The Scoutmaster sat himself down at the top of the Gully with a pair of field-glasses. Generally he acted as referee on these occasions, and rarely interfered during the progress of the game itself.

It was much better, and also more amusing, that Jimmy Spence should be allowed to turn his back to the foe in order to watch the antics of those two rabbits, and that he should be quietly stalked and scalped while so doing (Jimmy would be more careful next time); or that the entire pack of Lions should desert their section of the line and chivvy a solitary Otter while the Leader of the attack calmly passed through the gap so left—two excellent points to furnish his summing-up at the finish.

Presently far away up at Lone Pine he could see a flag waving, the pre-arranged signal that the dispatch had got through.

So he blew the rally on his whistle, and the tribe gathered to hear his words of wisdom.

"Leaders, got your notebooks?" he queried, when all had assembled and were looking down on the stricken field. "Good! Just make a note of what went wrong.

" Dan, that was quite an idea of yours wading through the reeds ; but you forgot all about the coots, didn't you ? They gave you away properly, and Jack nabbed you as you landed, didn't he ? One up to Jack for reading the sign of the startled coots.

" Jimmy, you showed yourself a proper Tenderfoot watching bunny-rabbits when you should have been looking out for Otters.

" Lions, I'm ashamed of you, losing your manes over one poor little Otter. You left one hundred and fifty yards clear gap, and Arthur slipped through. You did exactly as the wise Arthur expected. I hope you feel as silly as he made you look.

" Pigeons, nothing much came your way, but you hid well and kept quiet. Now, we are going to play this game again another day ; but, before we do, I want you three Leaders to take your Seconds and go all over the ground carefully.

" Get a plan formed in your heads both for attack and defence ; and don't let me see those same howlers made next time.

" So much for the game. Joe, just run on with your people and get tea ready. The other two lots spread out as we go back and see which Patrol can bring in the largest assortment of ground plants between here and camp."

Tea in camp on a hot afternoon after a vigorous game is very refreshing ; also it has the advantage of being a simple meal—no frying-pans or saucepans to clean.

By the time that our dusty and knee-pricked braves had got back to camp Joe was about ready for them.

Nor had Geoff been idle. He had kept his eye on the camp clock, and had put the kettle on to boil some time before ; he had swept and garnished the kitchen, gathered all the chips under the dry wood shelter, and re-stacked the logs.

A good Scout was Geoff. Not much to say for himself

—one of the silent sort—but always one of the first to volunteer for a job, and with the wit to do the right thing at the right time.

"What! kettle boiling already?" said the Scoutmaster. "Geoff, my son, you're a jewel! Heavens, Joe! they won't eat all that, will they?" as he surveyed a growing mountain of bread and jam.

"Won't we, sir?" quoth Jimmy Spence. "You just watch us."

"Shut up, Jim," Joe joined in. "Tenderfeet who lose their little scalps don't get no tea. We give 'em a dry crust to keep 'em alive—though it aren't worth doing even that in your case. Now, then, line up for your tea, you chaps. Otters first—they won!"

The merry meal began.

The period after tea in a Scout camp is generally a time of do-as-you-please—at least, it was so at Ripley Pool.

There are, however, one or two little jobs to be attended to first.

The water-supply must be made up, the milk fetched, the tent brailings let down, and the blankets brought in out of a possible dew.

After that the Troop dispersed until evening flag parade, and many and various were the occupations which the boys devised to fill the remaining hours of daylight.

Sam, for instance, was certain that he had found a real otter track by the ruined cottage, and borrowed the plaster-of-paris so that yet another cast might be added to the Troop collection.

Jimmy and Reggie Weekes went off to the village to buy sweets, laden with commissions for those who were too lazy to do it themselves. Arthur settled down to initiate Nobby into the mysteries of rope-spinning, while two or three took their rods to fish up at Caribou Creek.

The punt—a slow but safe craft—had been allotted

to the Lions for that evening, and was soon zigzagging and rocking its way across the placid water, propelled indifferently by a broken oar and two pieces of planking.

The Scoutmaster himself, after seeing that all was as it should be in camp, took his gun and made off with Joe in the direction of the bracken-clad bank away beyond the Gully to shoot rabbits for the pot.

And the camp was empty once more—empty except for Geoff, who sat by the fire and whittled away at a thumb-stick. Presently he noticed that the Scoutmaster's tent had not been put ready for the night; he also discovered that there was no water in the Scoutmaster's jug. So he put both matters right and returned to his thumb-stick and the guardianship of the fire.

To-morrow, he thought to himself, his knee should be well enough to let him go out with the rest of his Patrol on wood-getting, even perhaps to try for his high-diving test from the boat-house roof. Meanwhile it was very pleasant, after weeks of following a plodding team over miles of heavy clay and the methodical feeding of pigs and chickens, just to mess about camp and do odd jobs, gaze into the glowing embers and smell the good wood-smoke, and look forward to ten more days of utter contentment and happiness.

It is worth anything to be a Scout, thought Geoff, as he laid aside the completed thumb-stick and added two more logs to the fire. He had learnt something, too, since he had first joined up as raw a Tenderfoot as Jimmy Spence.

It seemed quite natural now to keen an axe and use it properly; to choose your wood, get it down, and trim it for loading without waste of time; to sleep in a bivvy tent with nought but two blankets and a ground-sheet; and to wake ready for a plunge into the deep, cold water of Ripley Pool.

And yet how he had funked washing even as much as his neck a few years back!—just as had Jimmy that morning.

What a lot he had picked up Scouting, when one came to add it all together! He could find his way across country by day or night, read a map, understand something of the mystery of the stars; and, when he came to the end of the trek, it seemed the simplest thing in the world to unsling his pack, cook supper, and go dry and warm to bed.

Then, again, it had been jolly useful to know all about cleaning and bandaging wounds when Sam had cut his leg that time they were hiking together for their First Class.

Yes, it was good to be a Scout, he decided. But what probably Geoff did not realise was that the doing of more than his own share of the work in camp, or the little acts of kindness and usefulness which had gradually become part of his nature, should also be added to the account of Scouting.

And yet when he looked back—it seemed ages ago—to the time when he was even as Jimmy Spence, and reviewed the years which lay between, his Scoutmaster seemed to have no very tangible connection with all this accumulation of knowledge and experience.

True, he was always there in the background, and, if there was any trouble, one could go to him and come away feeling that somehow the worry of it had gone, but his part in the proceedings had been quiet and unobtrusive.

He had always played fair, too—seemed to have no favourites, and yet be best friend to all the Troop.

There were certain things, of course, one had to do—not always pleasant things. If they were shirked, he had a way of making one never want to shirk again; and yet he never flared up or seemed to lose his temper. What he said, though, in that quiet way of his went straight home; and it was worth a lot to do something which pleased him.

Geoff wondered what it would be like when the time came for him to leave the Troop. There was some idea of his going to Canada, to an uncle who had a farm.

Well, anyhow, he determined, as he began to set out the bread and cheese for supper and rummaged in the store-tent for the cocoa-tin, they would be something to look back upon, these camps at Ripley Pool.

A few minutes later the object of his thoughts and Joe came down the slope from the old oak, bearing between them four rabbits.

While the three were busy cleaning these, the rest of the Troop wandered in by twos and threes, some sucking sweets and noisily happy, others displaying sundry small roach and perch (one of which, in the absence of any means of weighing it, was said to be at least a pound in weight). All were quite hungry again.

But before supper they assembled in orderly array round the flag and saluted it as it fluttered slowly to the ground. After that the Scoutmaster announced the programme for the following day.

"To-night," he added, "we are going to entertain the village to a sing-song. So we shall want a big circle and all the available logs and seats and ground-sheets. And remember, Scouts, hosts don't sit while their guests remain standing.

The sing-song was voted a great success. Not the least successful items were those contributed by Mr. Farmer and his small daughter—a rollicking song of the hunting-field and a morally uplifting (if shy) recitation.

There were solos on the penny whistle, several mouth-organ interludes, and a yarn by the Scoutmaster.

And the fire blazed and snapped, and sent showers of sparks up amongst the leafy branches overhead. The moon shone out of a cloudless sky, and even the myriad stars twinkled as if they were enjoying it too.

And then Mrs. Farmer said that it was really time they bade "Good-night," and she was going to bake a big cake and send it down the next day because they had enjoyed their evening so much.

And after they were gone home up the hill, heads were

bared for prayers, in which God's blessing was asked upon those near and dear to them, upon their brother-Scouts throughout all the world, and upon their own slumbers under the stars that night.

Shepherded by their Leaders, the Patrols faded away to their several camps; and yet another summer's day of happiness and well-directed energy had become but a memory.

Yet what a memory to add to the long list of others like it! thought the Scoutmaster, as he sat alone in the empty circle and smoked a last pipe before turning in.

And as he gazed into the glowing embers, he, too, like Geoff, reviewed the past and thought of the years ahead, when the boys whom he had known and loved through childhood to adolescence should be grown men and fighting their own battles.

What had he done for them? he asked himself. Would they go out any the better equipped for all the thought and work and guidance it had been such a happiness to give?

And then, as if in answer to the unspoken question, there came to him the recollection of incidents, small perhaps in themselves, but large with faith in the power of Scouting and in the part which he himself had been privileged to play.

So he sat on, and thought, and planned. And so still was he that two bold fox-cubs came up out of the wood to investigate the buried treasure of camp refuse.

And the owls resumed their interrupted conversations.

And the wise old moon smiled down upon all, as if to say:

> "A thousand camps such as yours sleep beneath my beams to-night. A thousand men are thinking and planning as do you. And thrice ten thousand boys are in their keeping. Friend, go forward in faith."

PRINTED IN GREAT BRITAIN BY
UNWIN BROTHERS LIMITED LONDON AND WOKING